The Secrets of the Hohenzollerns

WILLIAM I

Proclaimed emperor at Versailles in 1870—During the May
revolution when Prince of Prussia he was forced to
flee to England

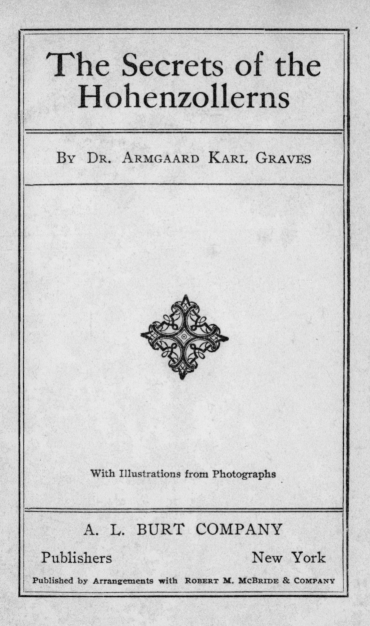

The Secrets of the Hohenzollerns

By Dr. Armgaard Karl Graves

With Illustrations from Photographs

A. L. BURT COMPANY

Publishers   New York

Published by Arrangements with Robert M. McBride & Company

FOREWORD

You say, "This is fiction."
I say it is not.
You say that I lie.
I say I do not.
Quien sabe?
My first book, "The Secrets of the German War Office," has been the target of much criticism. Some of the criticisms I appreciated and found more or less justified. Others, were too ill-informed and contemptible to represent even a casual judgment of the facts.

It appears that the purchase of a book entitles the buyer to criticize; be it so. Some unofficial representatives of governments, notably the German, have seen fit to attack me in their usual underhanded way. I understand their necessity for so doing. Also, I expected this, for I have been long enough in their employ to know the "wherefore" and the "why." I have made no answers to these attacks, for I hold, with the sages of old, that too strenuous a denial is the natural act of a guilty conscience. I do not ask for sympathy or tolerance, for neither has ever been mine, besides I can do very well without them.

Foreword

My veracity and morals have been, and will be doubted; well, that is my concern.

One thing I never have been, and that is a coward. I have taken the Persian Satrap's advice to his son:

> "My Son, if bad luck does pursue thee,
>   Yield not, though in courage you lack;
> A fighter goes scathless through battle
>   When a coward is shot in the back."
>
> GRAVES.

CONTENTS

PUBLISHERS' NOTE

In order to consolidate into a consecutive narrative the varied events in which the present two generations of the Hohenzollerns have taken part, the author has adopted the name of Bertram von Ehrenkrug. Under this pseudonym he is able to relate not only his own experiences but those of secret service agents who were working with him. The bulk of the missions, however, were undertaken solely by the author.

The Secrets of the Hohenzollerns

CHAPTER I

THE MESSAGE

Explanatory Note.—Whenever a King of Prussia lies on his death bed there is handed to his successor a small, time-scarred black ebony box, nine inches long by four inches wide. This box is sent immediately after the demise of the reigning King to the hereditary Truchsess of the Kingdom, who acknowledges its receipt by returning one of the only two existing keys to the secret royal archives. In these archives, accessible only to the King, the Truchsess and the Reichs Chancellor, are stored the innermost secrets of the Royal House and the Empire. Although officially the keeper of the King's secrets is never en evidence, unofficially and unobtrusively he wields a tremendous power, much as did in the olden days the keeper of the King's conscience.

IN the heart of the Mark of Brandenburg, called "The Streusand-Büchse" of Prussia, about fifty miles from Berlin, in the midst of one of the magnificently, well-cared-for Prussian domain forests, stands the hereditary castle of the Freiherren von Ehrenkrug. This stronghold is the seat of the Koenigliche Oberfoersterei, the officially known position of the Masters of Ehrenkrug, and the only one known to ninety-nine out of every hundred of their fellow men. To the remaining few, Derer von Ehrenkrug are of vastly greater significance. Since the days of the accession of the first Markgraf of Brandenburg, the House of Ehrenkrug has been closely identified with the aims, ambitions and successes of their Liege Lords of Hohenzollern. Even prior to this time, they were Reichsgraven and Truchsesses [1] in the old German Empire. They were kingmakers in the truest sense of the word.

Grim and silent, surrounded by historic oak and fir trees, stood the ancient castle of Ehrenkrug. On the night of June 15, 1888, a drizzling rain was falling upon the battle-scarred walls.

Grim and silent, swaying in the chilling blasts, stood the countless majestic trees like an outer guard, as if aware of portentous events.

---

[1] *Truchsess* literally means "sitting on the coffer." It is a medieval title of the most trusted official of the old Saxon kings and early German emperors.

The Secrets of the Hohenzollerns

Grim and silent, human sentinels, clad in the dark green and silver uniform of the Prussian Royal Foresters, were guarding the passage to the big oak-paneled refectory of the castle.

Around a solid wine-stained oak table were seated six men, reclining in deep leather cushioned arm chairs, their faces fitfully illuminated by a crackling log fire burning in a huge, brass-bound hearth. At the head of the table was a commanding figure, tall, six feet two in his stockings, wide of shoulder and deep of chest, with the traditional bearing and carriage of a Prussian officer; the big massive head framed with deep gold hair and beard, slightly streaked with gray; keen steel blue, clear eyes, set wide apart. Truly, a magnificent type of the Teuton, this, Wolfgang von Ehrenkrug, head of his house!

At his right sat an equally tall but more slender man, his South Germanic origin clearly indicated in his dark hair and eyes. Clean shaven, with thin-lipped, closely compressed mouth and high forehead, his severely intellectual, almost clerical aspect, easily stamped him for what he was—the Minister Plenipotentiary of the Bavarian court, Graf von P——. To the left was seated a short, stockily built, almost rubicund gentleman, whom one, even without glancing at his canonicals, or without looking at the gold cross suspended from his neck, or the big blood-red, gleaming carbuncle on the third finger of his right hand, would have pronounced a dignitary of the Church. And such he was, the Prince Bishop of Mayence.

Seated in the other chairs were three high officials of the German Empire. All their faces reflected deep, earnest, almost solemn thoughts. No one had uttered a word since they had been ushered into the hall by equally silent retainers, an hour before midnight. Only von Ehrenkrug, the head of the table, cast frequent glances at the big, dully-ticking Wanduhr. It struck the hour of twelve. Almost simultaneously the door opened and a somber-clad, gray-haired servant walked up to his master, and saluting, said in a trembling voice, "Gnädiger Herr, the messenger has come." Deep emotion was reflected in von Ehrenkrug's face and voice; as he arose, he placed his hand on the old servant's shoulder:

"It had to come, Herman."

Quietly sobbing, the servant retired from the circle of men and took his place in the back of the room. Turning to the others present, the Master, in his low, deep voice, said:

"Gentlemen, is it your pleasure to have the messenger sent in?" A silent nod was their answer. The watching servant, receiving the sign, almost immediately returned with the messenger, an officer of the Royal Household. All had arisen. Walking straight up to the Freiherr, the officer saluted, and handing him a small black ebony box, said at the same time:

"Der Kaiser ist todt." (The Emperor is dead.)

Although everyone in the room had expected this message for hours, all were visibly affected. The Freiherr had drawn from his closely buttoned coat a thick black silk ribbon, on which were suspended two curiously wrought silver keys, one of which he handed to the messenger, who, saluting, left. The door closed, the Freiherr turned to his waiting companions, saying:

"It behooves us to do our duty. Follow me."

Opening a door at the farther end of the hall he led them down a flight of narrow, stone stairs into the keep of the castle.

There in the flickering candlelight the six men gathered about a time-marred, brass-bound, cedar and sandalwood catafalque wrought with curious Sanscrit designs. Reverent and noiseless their movements. This was the catafalque in which was borne back to his home in 1040 the founder of the House of Ehrenkrug who had perished during the Crusades in a valiant attempt to save Wolfram of Heckingen, one of the noble ancestors of the Hohenzollerns. Ever since that day this coffin has been the repository for the most important documents of House and State.

Inserting a key into the ancient lock, Wolfgang von Ehrenkrug strove to throw the bolt. Years of idleness had stiffened the lock. But with oil and many manipulations the bolt was finally thrown.

The lid turned back, there appeared a black hole. The old Freiherr took up the black ebony box. Carefully he touched the edges with oil and gently he placed it in the hole. It fitted perfectly. A perceptible glance of relief passed over the faces of the group.

A moment later there was handed into the room two buckets of water. Wolfgang von Ehrenkrug motioned to his companions to stand back. As they withdrew he poured the water over the

box until the crevices were filled.[1] Then taking
a heavy wooden mallet, he struck the ebony box,
now in position, a sharp blow. With a clicking
noise a seam in the extreme right opened and dis-
closed a hollow compartment. Bending over, the
old Freiherr abstracted a zinc cylinder containing closely written parchments yellow with age.
These parchments were sealed with the great seal
of Prussia.

Calling his companions, he had them bear wit-
ness to the fact that the seals were intact and
unbroken.

Thereupon they signed a paper which the
Count placed with other similar vouchers in another compartment of the chest. Returning the
documents to their tube, he carefully abstracted
the ebony box, closed the lid and locked the outer
covering of the catafalque. A few moments
later the party was driven to the station, whence
a special train conveyed them to Berlin.

[1] A powerful deadly poison in the form of fine powder is
sprinkled freely between the outer lid and the inner secret cubicle
of the catafalque. The drenching eliminated the risk to those
acquainted with the secret. Those unacquainted with the secret
pay the price of their unwarranted trespass. On two distinct occasions attempts were made by unauthorized persons to delve into
this chest. Both were found dead alongside it.

CHAPTER II

THE NEW RÉGIME

BERLIN was cast in gloom. The usual rather boisterous gaiety of the Berliners was very much subdued. On Unter den Linden a fine drizzling rain made the great globes of the electric arc lights gleam as through a hazy nebula. A great rain-soaked throng of humanity moved slowly up to the Palace on the Schloss-Platz, becoming denser as it neared the royal residence where other masses of loyal citizens had stood for hours, awaiting the dread news. The idol of the German Empire, the hero of the Franco-Prussian War, the ideal of Teutonic manhood, lay dying. Anxiously every face was turned toward the flagstaff on the roof of the Palais, where the royal standard was drooping. A dim figure was seen fumbling with the halyards, and slowly the standard was lowered to half mast. The indistinct murmur of the vast crowd was instantly hushed, and with bared heads they listened to the booming

8

of the minute guns. Frederick III, Emperor of Germany, King of Prussia, lovingly called " Unser Fritz," was dead.

For the second time within one hundred and two days the Empire was cast into deep mourning. The new ruler, in certain sections feared and hated on account of supposed intolerance and ambition, was largely an unknown, but all-important factor in their destinies. No wonder anxious faces were lifted to the dim outline of the emblem of royal power.

Inside the Palais, in the anteroom leading to the royal death chamber, were assembled the principal office holders of the Empire, led by Fürst Bismarck, who stood nearest to the folding doors. He stood alone, evidently sunk in deep reflection. Curious glances and significant shoulder shrugs were directed toward him, plainly showing the rather ill-concealed thoughts of some of the courtiers present. Bismarck, the man of blood and iron, the Iron Chancellor, almost undisputed head in Prussia and Germany for nearly twenty years, awaited his new master. Portentous meeting, this. The folding doors were pushed back, and with short, jerky steps Prince Wilhelm of Prussia, who only in the last ten minutes had become King of Prussia and Emperor of Germany, stood before them.

A medium tall, slimly built, fair-haired young man, remarkable only by reason of his intensely sharp, clear, steel blue eyes and proud bearing. Almost insignificant in this group of exceptionally tall, broad-shouldered, imposing-looking, gray-haired men, he was nearly dwarfed by the masterful presence of the Iron Chancellor. Hardly noticing the deep obeisance of the dignitaries, he stood gazing for fully a minute at the maker of his empire. Bismarck, drawn to his full height, looked straight at his new king. Slowly a quiet, almost paternal, smile appeared on the ruggedly lined face of the Chancellor. A deep, nervous flush overspread the young king's countenance. What were the thoughts coursing through those two minds? The one, by hereditary, inalienable and, to his mind, divine right, emperor of forty million people, placed there by an accident of birth—the other, a master mind seen but once in a century, the instrument that made possible his elevation to imperial power. The smile and flush can easily be interpreted.

Bismarck took two steps toward the King. William II held out his hand. Bismarck bent over it, stooping low to imprint the kiss of homage. Then the young monarch, his blue eyes alight with pride, showed one of his rare flashes of intuition and tact by placing his arm around the Chancellor with an intimate gesture. Still keeping his left arm on Bismarck's shoulder, he turned to the others, saying:

"Gentlemen, the Kaiser, my father, *ist zur Ruhe gegangen.*"

Turning to Bismarck, he said in his sharp, rather shrill voice, "Your Excellency will issue all necessary orders and send out the summons."

With a wave of his hand he dismissed his audience, and, beckoning to Bismarck to follow him, he reentered the death chamber.

Six hours after the young emperor had led Bismarck to the bed of the dead king there was held in the Royal Palace a secret conclave. The King, Bismarck, von Ehrenkrug, and three others debated long behind closed doors which opened only when Wilhelm II and the tall Ehrenkrug descended into the royal archives. What transpired there no one (except the Emperor and von Ehrenburg) knows, for Wolfgang von Ehrenkrug had delivered to the new emperor the black box with the secrets of his house, secrets that were later to soak Europe in blood.

When Wilhelm II came up from the secret room he was a changed man. From a rather gay, somewhat dissipated, broad-minded Bohemian prince, Wilhelm II had changed mysteriously into a stern, almost puritanical king, with no thought but for his house and empire. He had read the message, the instruction that was to fashion his destiny.

Some, indeed most of those documents are in the handwriting of Frederick the Great. The exact purport is known only to those directly concerned and only given to the ascending kings.[1] It is a notorious fact that wars and acts of aggression are never entered into by the Hohenzollerns until they have reached the age of forty. This is of remarkable significance when history has shown us that acts of conquest are made at an extremely early age and in the first years of manhood when ideals and ideas pulse powerfully and run high. In the instances of Genghis Khan,

[1] The author wishes it clearly understood that his knowledge of these things is derived and pieced together solely from conversations overheard in his own family circle, from personal observation and disjointed scraps of documentary evidence which have at times passed through his hands. He does not claim a personal perusal or contact with the documents mentioned in this chapter.

The Secrets of the Hohenzollerns

Tamerlane, Alexander the Great, Attila and Bonaparte, their conquests were made in their early manhood, in some instances even in their teens. The history of the Hohenzollerns, with one or two exceptions, shows the distinct opposite. The empire and reign of these youthful conquerors has never lasted longer than the second or third generation, whereas the Hohenzollerns with ever-increasing power have reigned for nearly eight centuries. In natural traits and impulses they have the same tendencies of making their power and might felt, they have the same desire as is shown in the history of Frederick the Great and the attitude of the present heir apparent to give to primeval and martial instincts. Nevertheless, these desires are curbed and undergo a complete change on attaining supreme command. William II made no exception to this mysterious influence.

The first act of the young kaiser after his view of the contents of that box was to place his own mother under arrest.

Now, between Wilhelm II and his mother, no love was ever lost. The reason for this dormant ill-feeling goes back many years. When he was about two years of age, his mother, then Crown

The Secrets of the Hohenzollerns

Princess Frederick, rigidly adhered to her English habits, one of these being her daily morning ride. These rides were looked upon rather askance, as it was not the custom for princesses of the Prussian court to show their equestrian abilities. Her Royal Highness also had a habit of taking her little son in front of her saddle, all remonstrances being of no avail. On one of these morning constitutionals, having to manage a rather restive animal, she dropped the infant. Somewhat alarmed, in view of the antagonistic attitude of the Court toward these morning canters, the accident was not mentioned and no medical attendance was called in at the time. After about three weeks, alarming symptoms appearing in the left arm and one side of the young prince, professional advisers were summoned. They had come too late; muscular atrophy resulting from a fracture had set in. Hence dates the Emperor's crippled left arm. Wilhelm II, intense admirer of all perfection, physical and otherwise, never forgave his mother.

It was not likely then that, suspecting his mother of having appropriated one of the most important documents from the secret archives of the Hohenzollerns, Wilhelm II would blush at drastic measures. Wherefore there came a conference with von Ehrenkrug. The Emperor imprisoned his mother in the palace. She was under guard—polite guard, to be sure, but utterly unyielding—for two days. At the end of that time Wolfgang von Ehrenkrug was summoned. Imprisonment had effected the desired result. The document was restored.

Freiherr Wolfgang von Ehrenkrug was seated in his study, reading the daily newspapers just arrived from the capital, a frown on his forehead getting deeper and deeper. The news contained in the papers was of an alarming nature. Sweeping changes were taking place in the army and civil cabinets. The martial, and somewhat bombastic, utterances of the new Emperor, had created a lot of ill-feeling in France. Affairs, up to now solely directed by Bismarck in an even, if iron tenor, were becoming unsettled through his continual clashing with the new imperial will. Bismarck, long used to undisputed sway and a free hand, was becoming more or less handicapped by the Emperor's growing habit of personally conducting affairs of state, and a break, sooner or later, became daily more apparent.

The Secrets of the Hohenzollerns

Von Ehrenkrug's perusal of the papers was disturbed by a servant announcing a visitor, who proved to be the Minister of Police, a cabinet officer of high rank, Count von P——. Von Ehrenkrug and the minister were life-long friends and comrades-in-arms. Von P—— unburdened himself without hesitation.

" Things are moving fast in the capital, Ehrenkrug. We've got a new master with a vengeance. Every report goes to him direct, instead of to the Chancellory. There's a deal of disappointment amongst his old cronies. I've had instructions to intimate to quite a few of them that a change of air—considerable air—would be very beneficial for their health." Bending forward, he said in a tense whisper, "He's inaugurating his own private Secret Service; messengers of his own choosing are coming and going hourly. The ambassadors to St. Petersburg and the Quai d'Orsay are being recalled. Changes, Ehrenkrug."

Von Ehrenkrug had listened in silence, nodding his head now and then. Now, raising his head, and looking his old friend straight in the face, he quietly remarked:

EMPRESS FREDERICK III. AND THE PRESENT
KAISER, AS PRINCE WILLIAM OF PRUSSIA

"And the object of your visit, *Alter Freund,* is what?"

The Minister of Police fidgeted somewhat, and after a slight hesitation said:

"It is about your nephew. Have you heard from him lately?"

Receiving a negative reply, he continued:

"Well, the young fool has been at it again. He has compromised himself to such an extent that a prolonged absence would be very advisable. I have received, so far, no official orders, and it is only on account of our long friendship that I am here to advise you in this matter. Your nephew, as you may or may not be aware, has identified himself with the Revolutionary Socialistic Party, and has been indiscreet enough to advocate their radical theories, not only in speeches, but in writings—brilliant writings, I must admit—but nevertheless highly dangerous, bound to come to the Emperor's notice. I would advise you to use your influence to stop this foolishness, or send him out of the country."

Von Ehrenkrug had listened without comment, and now simply said, "Thank you, old friend."

Touching a bell, he instructed the answering

servant to telegraph immediately to the young Freiherr at the University of Bonn to return home at once. . . .

The railway station at Furstenwalde an der Spree is small and sleepy. It is not a usual stopping-place for express trains, so that when the eastbound through train slowed down and came to a halt it drew quite a few curious onlookers. A young man descended, carrying overcoat and cane. The station master gave a startled look, then rushed forward, giving the youth an effusive greeting, which was returned in a very debonnair manner. Most of the idlers gathered also extended familiar, yet very respectful, greetings, and one of them being asked by a stranger, "Who is this young man? He seems pretty popular," was informed with no little pride of tone and gesture, "That's our young Freiherr, Bertram von Ehrenkrug." The station master, who knew young Bertram since he was knee-high, expresse his wonderment at the sudden appearance of t Freiherr, at the same time querying about lug gage and means of transportation, to all of which queries he received the laughing answer, "Oh, the Governor wired for me and, *Donnerwetter,* I've left my grip in the train. I forgot to let them know at home that I was coming by this train. You had better telegraph to the Schloss and have them send in the dog cart. I am going over to the Black Eagle Inn."

All of which was very characteristic of Bertram Erwin, hereditary Freiherr and heir of Derer von and Zu Ehrenkrug, for a more unconventional, Bohemian scion the rather staid, conventionally conservative and proud House of Ehrenkrug had never produced. This trait of character, manifested since the early childhood of Bertram, was a continual source of discord between him and the head of the house. Bertram was soon comfortably ensconced in the beer garden fronting the inn, and quickly surrounded by a coterie of old cronies, hugely enjoying their gossip. All too soon the dog cart drove up. All too soon, for Bertram had a decidedly uneasy feeling in regard to his sudden summons home. He was received by his uncle's own body servant, upon whose countenance, at no time cheerful, rested an extra funereal gloom. With a muttered "B-rr, the weather gage points to storm. I'm in for it," he walked into his uncle's study.

The old Freiherr was standing in front of the

fireplace. Acknowledging the salute of his nephew with a curt nod, he queried, "Have you eaten, Bertram?" receiving an equally curt, "Yes, thanks, sir."

There was no hint of familiarity or close relationship in their attitude. Notwithstanding, they bore a striking resemblance to each other. Bertram was as tall as his uncle, but of slimmer build. The same widely set-apart blue eyes, the same high forehead and firmly molded chin, in the case of the younger man as yet softer and unlined. Without preamble, his uncle began:

"I suppose you know why I have recalled you from your university?" Without waiting for an answer, he continued:

"I have received a visit from Count von P——, who unofficially informed me that your activities have attracted the seriously displeased attention of the Government. It is only your position as my nephew and heir to the House of Ehrenkrug and the personal friendship to me of the Minister of Police, that has saved you from most serious consequences. Von P—— warned me that the Emperor's attention was bound to be drawn toward you. I intended to send you abroad, but Von P——'s warning came too late. I received, this morning, a peremptory order from the Emperor for your instant removal from the University. You are to report yourself to the Military Kadetten-Anstalt of Lichterfelde within forty-eight hours. You can count yourself fortunate, for instead of a punishment, it is more of an honor.

"Not a word!" the Freiherr commanded, raising his hand in a gesture of silence. "I know what you wish to say. We have gone over all this before. I know your ideals about being a free agent and leading your own life. You are not a free agent, and you cannot lead your own life. You have to pay the penalty—if penalty it is—of being born into the House of Ehrenkrug, which for five hundred years has observed tradition and served its rulers and country with unsullied honor and fidelity. Be silent!" the Freiherr exclaimed again, as he noticed an attempt on the part of Bertram to interrupt him. "Your free thought ideals and tendencies you have without doubt derived from your mother, who, excellent woman though she was, could never control her hot, independent, Polish blood, and to my intense sorrow she has bequeathed you her temperament. You will from now on be subjected to an iron military discipline, which will teach you obedience, the first rule neccessary in those who wish to command others. This is your last chance, for although the House of Ehrenkrug has always sufficient power and influence to advance and protect, this power would never be used for the benefit of an unruly member of the family. You will clearly understand this. That is all. Go to your quarters."

Bowing to his uncle, and turning on his heel, Bertram walked out. Like the Emperor, his star was not yet in the zenith.

CHAPTER III

DROPPING THE PILOT

"Tempora mutantur
Et mutantur tempora."

THE times were changing with a vengeance.
Quite a few, however, found it impossible
to change with the times set by the new sun. Unlike the ruler of the solar constellation, Wilhelm
II made the seasons go in anything but celestial
regularity. One thing both rulers had in common: as the heavenly luminary exerts an absolute sway over her satellite, so does the earthly
monarch demand an absolute subvergence to his
will. He, *von Gottes Gnaden* (by the grace of
God), King of Prussia and Emperor of Germany,
would not brook an empire within an empire.

The Court on the Spree, in particular, and the
Empire in general was seething. William II had
taken a firm grip. More than any of his prede-
cessors; in fact, not since the days of Frederick

the Great had any monarch taken such a personal hold of affairs. Every department of state was on the constant *qui vive;* no garrison within two hundred miles of Berlin was safe from midnight alarms; reforms were the order of the day. Publicly fond of pomp and display, which he considered commensurate with his imperial dignity, the Emperor personally observed a Spartan frugality, and insisted upon the same in others. He was deadly opposed to over-indulgence, especially gambling, which had become somewhat prevalent amongst the feudal Prussian aristocracy, particularly in the officers' *kasino* (mess) of the crack regiments.

While he was still Prince of Prussia he had been appointed Colonel of the First Dragoon Guards by his grandfather, Emperor Wilhelm I. The regiment was then stationed at Potsdam. The young colonel paid the regiment one of his midnight surprise visits. He found a large majority of his brother officers in a pretty advanced carousal, roulette and baccarat tables well patronized. Prince Wilhelm placed the whole lot under instant arrest and had them confined to quarters. Every one of those officers was connected with the leading Prussian aristocracy, having a great deal of political influence and social prestige. The old emperor was privately approached to intercede for them. He summoned his nephew and suggested that the incident be overlooked.

Prince Wilhelm quietly asked his grandfather: "Am I Colonel of the First Dragoon Guards?"

"You certainly are," he was told.

"Am I responsible for the regiment?"

"Without doubt."

The young prince slowly unbuckled his sword and holding it out to the Emperor, saluting, said:

"I tender Your Majesty my resignation as Colonel of the Prussian Dragoon Guards No. 1."

The startled, but secretly much-pleased old Emperor refused the resignation. When the fathers and friends of the disgraced officers again approached His Imperial Majesty, they were told:

"I am quite willing to be lenient, but, you see, the Colonel is not." A goodly number of the officers were broken and exiled.

The Court itself was divided into three distinct factions. The first, led by Bismarck, was composed of gray-haired members of the two previous régimes, accustomed to having their own way in conducting affairs as they had done under the old Emperor William I, and the ill and easy-going Frederick III.

The second faction was grouped around the Empress Frederick III, who, prior to her marriage to Frederick III, then Crown Prince of Prussia, was Princess Royal of England, being the eldest child of Queen Victoria. A typical, cold, proud English woman, she never quite found her place in the Prussian royal court. Accustomed to considerable political power and influence in her home country and at her mother's court, she never ceased trying to graft English ideas upon the Prussian court, with rather disastrous results to herself and supporters, for soon after the ascension of Wilhelm II to the throne she went into almost complete retirement. The misunderstanding between Wilhelm II and his mother has often been used by the enemies of the Emperor to his disparagement. This has a certain justification, for while he accorded to his mother a deferential attitude, due to her as Empress Mother, Wilhelm II, ever being a stickler for etiquette, at no time pretended to be a loving son—why, you already know.

The third faction was of the Emperor's own selection, men of the younger generation, of a new era, and with a more pronounced commercial instinct. A *Neuer Zeitgeist* (new spirit of the times) was setting in, and Wilhelm II thoroughly identified himself with this spirit—contrary to the approval of Bismarck's faction.

It was inevitable that there came a day when in the Reichskanzler Palast (the official residence of the Chancellor) in Berlin an air of great excitement was apparent. Secretaries, privy counsellors and ministers were coming and going or standing about in groups in the numerous antechambers of the palace. The conference chamber leading immediately into Fürst Bismarck's study was filled with the leaders of the Imperial Diet and the principal members of their respective parties.

Low-toned but eager conversation was going on. The greater number of the groups, composed of the older men, were mostly friends of the old chancellor, used to and versed in the methods of their chief and leader. Little wonder that they cast anxious looks toward the door leading into the old lion's den. Other groups, representing the younger generation and the new era, notably those of the Left Center, the Clericals, were plainly elated. The heavy heel of the man of iron was going to be lifted; the pin pricks and machinations of the parties opposed to Bismarck's policies were at last to take effect. Hence, their elation. The gespannte *Stimmung* (strained sympathy) between the Emperor and his chancellor was on the breaking point. This, to a certain extent, was undoubtedly due to Bismarck's uncompromising attitude toward the new spirit of the time.

A typical leader and exponent of the iron-clad Prussian *Junker* class, he showed an unyielding front toward the awakening and restless commercial spirit of the new Germany. By birth, breeding, natural tendencies, and habit, Bismarck was the embodiment of radical conservatism. His immense superiority over all his contemporaries and his signal successes in welding the North German confederation into a cohesive empire, besides his dominant personality, had made him the idol of the German people. Used to unrestricted power and almost absolute control under the régimes of William I and Frederick III, the active interference in his policies by the young emperor were treated by Bismarck with scant tolerance. At no time choice in his expressions against those in opposition, Bismarck more than once voiced criticisms about the new emperor, which were drastic to say the least. These remarks, judiciously exaggerated, were promptly transmitted to His Imperial Majesty by the Chancellor's enemies, and were, to a great extent, responsible for Bismarck's brusk retirement.

Another factor which conspired toward his downfall, a factor whose power many equally great men have found out too late, was the antagonizing of the Church. The Church has had, has now, and always will have, a tremendous influence in national affairs. Outstanding figures in history have been able to use religion, domineer it, even subjugate it; but only for a time. This applies to all denominations, more especially to the established Catholic Church, most so to the followers of Loyola (Jesuits), the militant section of the Church of Rome. Bismarck, in the zenith of his power, deemed it necessary to crush its radical influence in Germany, and did so in his usual relentless manner.

An incident in Bismarck's career showing his iron hand may not be inappropriate here. The

Chancellor had curtailed the prerogatives and holdings of the Catholic churches in Germany to a great extent, the hardest hit being the institution and properties of the Brothers of Jesus. The Catholic Church, more especially this particular branch thereof, never submits to affronts without a struggle, and a bitter struggle it became. Their splendid organization opposed Bismarck to such an extent that he soon found it necessary to crush them, as he thought, completely. He confiscated their entire land holdings, taxed their properties, and put their institutions, such as colleges and seminaries, under direct state control. He also exiled and drove out of Germany about fifty per cent. of their officials. A threat was made to Bismarck that unless he repealed those orders, his life would be forfeited. The threat was, unfortunately, followed by a desperate attack: the Roman Catholic Kullman, a tinsmith, made a violent attack on Bismarck at Kissingen. This deed was done in a white fury of Ultramontane anger, engendered by the May laws, and in no wise can be attributed to any branch of the Church. The Order of the Jesuits are not Maffias or blackhanders; their summons is never an idle one. This attack by

Kullman, however, resulted in even more stringent restrictions being placed on Jesuitical institutions. Bismarck did not treat the ultimatum lightly. Within forty-eight hours a double military post was stationed outside the domicile of every prominent dignitary, such as priests, rectors, and vicars. They had strict orders to shoot every designated person in the event of Bismarck being assassinated . . . Bismarck died a natural death . . .

There was a clatter of hoofs and a rattle of arms outside the portals of the palace. Inside, the whispering groups became still. The attendants were hurrying to their posts. The portals were thrown open and the chief usher announced, *"Seiner Majestät der Kaiser."*

William II, curtly acknowledging the salute of the assembled gentlemen, walked without pause directly into the Chancellor's private chamber. Bismarck was seated at his desk in the historic, double-bay windows. He was sitting with his head resting on his hand, in deep thought. From the two private secretaries at their desks at the other end of the room came never a sound. The sudden opening of the door and the springing to attention of the secretaries drew Bismarck's attention. This appearance of the Emperor's unannounced and unexpected presence in his quarters was plainly an unwelcome surprise. It was one of His Majesty's famous surprise visits, which earned him the sobriquet of "Wilhelm der Plötzliche" (William the Sudden). Bismarck did not rise till the Emperor was directly in front and had addressed him with a sharp, "Well?"

Slowly and heavily he rose and looked down upon his king. In a weary, almost toneless voice, in striking contrast to his usual metallic utterances, the Chancellor said these words: "I will not retract, so under these circumstances, Your Majesty must do as he sees fit."

The Emperor, plainly angered, started an explosive sentence: "Well, then, I demand your—" Suddenly he checked himself, and turning around to the secretaries, who were still standing at their respective desks, ordered them to leave the room. What subsequently transpired between those two men is only known to themselves. The tense dignitaries in the anterooms were kept waiting for fully two hours before the Emperor reappeared.

Bismarck conducted the Kaiser to his carriage. Nothing in the attitude or facial expression of either the Emperor or the Chancellor gave the slightest indication of what had happened at this historic conference. The different political factions and parties assembled were profoundly puzzled; and when the Emperor in taking leave of his Chancellor placed his arm with an affectionate gesture on Bismarck's shoulder, saying in a tone of voice easily heard by all those in the room: "I trust that Your Excellency's health will improve, and that God will spare you to me and my country," the previously ill-suppressed air of elation in certain circles disappeared as if by magic.

The Emperor's pretended friendship for Bismarck deceived every one. Had there existed in Bismarck the slightest disloyalty to the House of Hohenzollern, however, the Iron Chancellor could have made himself master of Germany in name as well as in fact. But there was in Bismarck the true obedience to the iron law of feudal self-effacement for the common weal, and so he stepped down into oblivion.

Only after Bismarck's return to his chamber on the historic day of the Emperor's visit and his refusal to be seen, did pointed hints and conjectures begin making their rounds. Notwithstanding these conjectures, hints, and gossip, it was five days afterwards that the first indications of a serious break between the Iron Chancellor and the Emperor became known; and, curiously enough, via England. It is a strange fact, which has puzzled quite a few, why Sir John Tenniel, the famous British cartoonist, was able to publish his historic cartoon in *Punch* ("Dropping the Pilot") almost simultaneously with Bismarck's resignation. The reason why may be interesting to know. At that time, March 18, 1890, the Emperor, always more or less in the good graces of his grandmother, Victoria the Good, was distinctly *persona grata* at the Court of St. James. Bismarck, for many reasons, not the least of them being his blunt antagonism toward the Dowager Empress Frederick III, the Ex-Princess Royal of England (eldest daughter of Queen Victoria), was distinctly the reverse. The Emperor, in his usual impulsive way, had written to his grandmother his intention to break with Bismarck. Sir John Tenniel, a frequent guest at Windsor, happened to be present when this matter was discussed at the royal tea table, and promptly made use of this splendid opportunity to create one of his inimitable pen satires.

The complete break between Bismarck and the

DROPPING THE PILOT

Sir John Tenniel's historic cartoon which appeared in
"Punch" twenty-four hours before Bismarck's
resignation

Emperor created a profound sensation, not only in Germany, but throughout the whole civilized world. The acts of William II have been and are much criticized, but no single act of his begat so much adverse comment or aroused such bitter feeling. Without presuming or encroaching upon the task of the historian, it is but just to observe the real conditions. As previously indicated, Bismarck's economic methods had become somewhat antiquated. He did not understand and was not in sympathy with the growing commercial ambition of the new Germany and its young ruler. His arbitrary rule and iron hand had antagonized large and powerful factions, notably the Blacks, the Left Center, and the Clericals. Add to this his personal domineering arrogance as against the Emperor's ambitious intolerance, and it will be easily seen that such a state of affairs was impossible. Bismarck's service and achievements for his house and empire were always unstintingly acknowledged by William II. He created and made Fürst Bismarck the Herzog of Lauenburg, with the title of prince. Bismarck, who was not rich, received a magnificent estate out of the Emperor's private property. The Emperor, contrary to his usual habit, repeatedly sought after Bismarck, and any ill-feeling between those two was of Bismarck's own nursing. It is a curious trait in the House of Hohenzollern that they were ever ungrateful masters but stanch personal friends; but personal friendship and regard is never permitted to stand in the way of what they conceive to be to the advantage of their house or country. As the late Prince Hohenlohe said, shortly before his retirement, Wilhelm became the coolest rationalist, the greatest egotist, and the most ungrateful person he had ever met.

Without doubt William II has fostered that spirit of braggadocio which has led the German nation to believe its manifest destiny to be the leading power in the world. His own egotistical and arrogant ways were apparent long before he ascended the throne. There is every reason to believe that these inherited tendencies were further aggravated through his close identification with the most objectionably feudal, aristocratic, student corps, the *Borussia,* while at the University of Bonn. This is clearly indicated in the extreme partiality shown to all his old *Kommiltonen* (fellow students), of that association. To be a *Borussen* was an open sesame to the highest court positions in the gift of the young Kaiser.

The Secrets of the Hohenzollerns

Apart from these reasons, which are salient, Bismarck's dismissal can also be traced to the fact that the trend and tendency of the time demanded concessions be made from the throne to the Church. The growing socialistic propaganda was blocking the ambitious schemes of the Emperor to a great extent. The conspiracy against Bismarck had begun as early as 1885, and it is a striking fact that for five years after his dismissal Bismarck's name was not permitted to be mentioned in the Reichstag—the very body that he himself had created. This non-support of Bismarck by the Center, the Clerical Party, made the passing of the army and especially the navy bills impossible.

Bismarck's successor, Count von Hohenlohe-Schillingsfuerst, was a scion of an illustrious Catholic family, which had provided many prominent dignitaries to that faith. The immediate result of the Emperor's clever pacification of the powerful Center was the passing of the much-disputed army and navy appropriations. With true Hohenzollern insight, stimulated by the concentrated experience and advice stored in the royal secret archives, the Emperor has managed not only to get but to retain the good will and support of the Catholic Church; an unobtrusive, almost invisible support, nevertheless one of the most potent factors in the affairs of nations. How this support was gained and strengthened the reader can readily follow in the movements of the Kaiser and the attitude of the Church.

The successors of Peter have always deemed it advisable to support the most virile imperial power extant. The chief paradox of the situation was this: The Church, although professing to hold itself aloof from all temporal matters, realized that it could flourish only on direct authority and tradition, and consequently defended and supported the old established order, and therefore always allied itself with the most powerful and strongest to uphold its dignity. When Spain became decadent it shifted this support to France; after the French Revolution, the Emperor of Austria became titular protector of the Vatican; but there is no person or business on earth so quick in finding the weak spot as those at the helm of Christ's trireme. Austria, with its forty-two million souls of different racial tendencies and ambitions, was soon found to be rather an insecure anchoring ground. Germany's sixty-five cohesive millions, rapidly progressing in physical and material wealth, offered safer harborage. Bismarck, the storm center of the *Kulturkampf* and the main obstacle to a closer understanding, having been removed, overtures from the Vatican to the Court on the Spree found a harmonious reception . . .

The royal train in white and pale-blue enamel with the Prussian eagle embossed on each side was pulling out of the *Lehrter* (depot) in Berlin. This train would be conspicuous even in America, the land of railroad travel *par excellence*. It is invariably composed of five cars: the first containing railway and service officials; the second, the Emperor's immediate suite; the middle, the Emperor's coach; the fourth, dining and library car; and the last, the kitchen and lavatories. The Emperor's coach is the consummation of elegance and comfort. It is upholstered in silver brocade with dark rosewood facings, the dome solid panes of cut crystals, through which the electric bulbs filter the light with a soothing rainbow effect. There is one corner of this coach, however, severely plain. It contains the Emperor's cot and work table; here the paneling is oak and here is his iron bedstead with a mattress, the texture of which, if provided by the Pennsylvania Railroad, would call forth a flood of protest.

There is no break in the stern regularity of the Emperor's business life while he travels, for *Vortragende-Räte* (eminent men of letters, art, science, etc., who receive the honor and dignity of counselors) invariably accompany the Emperor on his travels, and hours, of necessity unoccupied, are filled with discussions on the latest achievements in the various artistic, literary, and scientific fields of the world. To this excellent practise of the Emperor's is due his reputation as a universal genius, for he has an excellent memory and can repeat almost *verbatim* even lengthy essays. Apropos of the German emperor's well-known proclivity for travel, the following query, which landed the author thereof for six months in durance vile, went the rounds in certain universities: "What are the attributes of the three German emperors, William I, Frederick III, and William II?" The answer: "The Good Kaiser, the Mute Kaiser, and the Route Kaiser."

The Emperor travels fast, and, of course, has the right of way over everything. There is always a pilot engine five hundred yards in front of the imperial train and also a rear-guard engine at the same distance behind. Since an attempt made in 1896 to wreck the imperial train, the exact time and route of the Kaiser's special is never published, and known only to the officials concerned.

Rome was in gala attire. Was not William II, Emperor of Germany, coming to visit their beloved Humbert? Thus thought the populace.

In reality, the visit of the Kaiser had quite another significance. Eight hours after the state banquet given in his honor at the Quirinal, he was quietly driven to the Vatican. The goblins surmounting the Cardinals' entrance must have grinned with an added touch of sardonic humor when William II, Emperor of Germany, passed through the portals. Eighteen months previous, Bismarck at the hottest period of the *Kulturkampf* (battle of culture) made use of this historic phrase: *"Nach Canossa gehen wir nicht"* (We won't go to Canossa). He referred to the historic incident when Henry IV, Emperor of Germany, excommunicated by Pope Gregory VII (Hildebrand) in 1077, was compelled to pilgrimage to Italy and stand barefooted in the snow whilst His Holiness pronounced his absolution.

Here, eight hundred years afterwards, another wielder of the *Reichs-Scepter,* the emblem of Germanic power, found it advisable to have speech with another pope. The goblins grinned! Wise goblins; yours has often been the privilege to see confirmed that old saying of the Eternal City, "All roads lead to Rome!"

The audience between His Holiness Leo XIII, Bishop of Rome, Keeper of the Keys of St. Peter, Pontiff of all Christendom, and William II, King of Prussia and Emperor of Germany, the most influential monarch of his time, was significant of the changing attitude and politics of the central European Power. It was far reaching in its consequences—for William II, fully recognizing the value of the Church's support, tacitly agreed that when the time came he would actively support the restoration of temporal power of the popes of Rome, a far-sighted, keen piece of diplomacy. Events are showing clearly that the princes of the Church, headed by Benedict, have been making supreme efforts to keep Italy from joining the Allies.[1] The Kaiser avoided Napoleon III's

[1] The late James T. Creelman, that dean of foreign correspondents, in a conversation with the author years ago in Rome clearly showed his marvelous insight and grip of foreign situations by correctly forecasting the benefit of the Emperor's visit to Rome.

grievous mistake in trying to outgeneral the most astute and seasoned diplomats in Europe. Napoleon in all probability would never have lost his throne but for his ill-advised policy of oscillating between the Italian government and the Church state. He would not agree to Italy's demand that the temporal power of the popes be abolished; on the other hand, his lukewarm promises to the political faction lost him the goodwill and support of the Church of Rome. If the Jesuit advisers of the Empress Eugénie had been followed, the history of the Franco-Prussian War would have been written in different terms.

The Emperor at the time was bitterly assailed in his own realm and the target of much buffoonery in other lands. To-day those who run may read—and they will have to change their opinion

Mr. Creelman was the only newspaper man who ever interviewed His Holiness. The information which he gained on this memorable occasion he never divulged to the public but he freely discussed this subject with the author who had obtained the same information from other channels. Mr. Creelman on many occasions interviewed and met the highest personages in Europe as an emissary of the United States government. It was known that he was a newspaper correspondent, but such was the confidence placed in this gentleman that his bare promise not to print any of the information thus gained in his publications was sufficient. These confidences were never abused. The standing of this quiet, unassuming American amongst the titled, be-ordered European diplomats was truly unique.

as regards the waning temporal power of the Church. This visit to the Pope was without doubt one of the best advised coups the Emperor has ever undertaken. Although made not purely on his own initiative, and, there is some reason to think, without a great deal of enthusiasm for the mission, his pilgrimage was in strict adherence to the laws of the Hohenzollerns, which, like the laws of the Medes and Persians, alter not nor change; laws that have been unswervingly followed for the best of their house and country, no matter at what cost, since the days of the Markgraf of Brandenburg.

An ardent advocate of a greater Germany, the Emperor successfully used his power to obtain colonies, such as German East Africa, the Kamerun, Kiao-Chau and Samoa. He became the father of the German navy, which up to his coming to the throne constituted half a dozen antiquated war vessels. As early as 1892, in Hamburg, the Emperor in one of his famous speeches used the almost prophetic words, *"Deutschland's Zukunft liegt auf dem Wasser"* (Germany's future lies on the water), indicating clearly that even at this early date he had formulated a definite policy of expansion, which he never lost sight of for a moment. At first the feeling of the German people toward this policy was less than lukewarm, but the fast-growing commerce and the necessities and benefits arising therefrom soon gave the Emperor increasing support. This support became solid after the *Hertzog* incident.

During the Boer War the German East African liner *Hertzog*, flying the postal flag of the German Empire, created an international incident. Without any apparent rime or reason it was chased by a British cruiser and stopped off Delagoa Bay. The Englishmen boarded the steamer which was protected by the imperial flag of Germany, and subjected it to a thorough search.

When the Emperor was informed of the affair he at once saw the opportunity. He cleverly employed it to further his plans. The press was inspired to print articles which caused intense indignation and public feeling. The national pride of a German is tremendous and when he read in his newspaper that the English, ruling the seas with a high hand, had stopped the imperial mail steamer, he grew wrathy about it at his café table. Subtly it was conveyed to him in the public prints that if Germany had a powerful navy England would not dare to stop the German flag on the high seas. And then, with his characteristic instinct for the dramatic, the Emperor appeared in the Reichstag. In terse, sledge-hammer language he demanded the support of the deputies for his naval policy. With Berlin in a furore over the *Hertzog* incident, the deputies yielded. The Emperor did not get all he asked for, but it was quite sufficient so that he was able to build up his navy until it became from a fifth rate, the second naval power in the world.

The natural consequences of the removal of Bismarck, the visit to Italy, and the large increase in the strength of the German army and navy created an unsettled feeling at home and a deep distrust abroad; especially in France. France had viewed with not a little alarm the rapidly increasing armament of her northern neighbor, and the Emperor's picturesque saber-rattling and dramatic utterances by no means allayed her trepidation. The French attitude was anything but displeasing to the Emperor just then, as it detracted public attention to a great extent from home affairs and gave him sufficient time to make sure and perfect his next move.

The Emperor and his policies had no real desire to quarrel with France just then, but there was a pronounced adverse feeling in France headed by that implacable antagonist to all things Germanic, Delcassé, who later with the able assistance of Edward VII made capital out of this situation to bring France and England into a closer alliance. The Emperor soon recognized the active influence of Delcassé and used his influence and power to such an extent that France at that time, to avoid the most serious consequences, agreed to the retirement of one of the most able men she has produced. The story of how Delcassé's downfall came about, of course, is a matter of common knowledge.

Now it was about this time that Bertram von Ehrenkrug finished his studies at the military academy with becoming docility and honor, and was in due time commissioned as a lieutenant to the Second Guard Uhlans, garrisoned in Berlin. Through the influence of his uncle he was given special opportunity to see much of the various European courts and capitals. Thanks to an assured social position and ample means, he made good use of his opportunities. Studious and observant, he acquired a remarkable fund of knowledge of men and manners of the countries visited. Of a naturally sunny and tactful, almost Bohemian, disposition, he was universally popular and soon a marked man to his superiors. All of which was necessary for the work which the fates had intended this young man should do. Then came a summons from the Emperor. The three ladies accredited with weaving the web of life were weaving fast—weaving intrigue and brooding war, for the young scion of the house of Ehrenkrug and the red secret of the Hohenzollerns were to move through the years on converging roads.

CHAPTER IV

THE STORMY PETREL

TA-TARI-TA-TA!

Four clear musical notes of a motor horn, used only by the Emperor in person.

"Achtung!" (attention). The Mounted Police hold up their hands. In the Unter den Linden all traffic stops. The flash of a bright yellow motor, the Prussian eagle in black and red on both doors, a glimpse of three men in plain dark blue and silver livery, and William II, King of Prussia, Emperor of Germany, Hertzog of Langenburg, Burggraf of Nuremburg, to quote but four of his forty titles, thunders past. Frantic haste and energy is expressed in the Emperor's mode of traveling. It is characteristic of the man, however, that, in spite of his intolerance of delays, he makes way and gives precedence to the fire brigade of Berlin.

"'Raus!" A rattle of drums, a click of presenting arms, and the car dashes through the por-

49

tals of the Kaiserlicher Palast on the Schloss Platz. With quick, nervous steps the Emperor walks past the palace guard, his right hand on the visor of his helmet, into his home.

On the right hand side of the first inner court-yard is an unpretentious, short, marble staircase, known as the *Kurfürsten* (Elector's) entrance, which the Emperor invariably uses. It does not matter how tired he is, he always walks up the twenty-six steps leading to his own quarters, often to the great annoyance and distress of some fat, short-winded, feeble-legged *Ratlente* (Coun-sellors). If accompanied, members of his suite, unless of the royal family or of the privy council, invariably remain in the first chamber, the *Orangen Zimmer* (Orange room).

Without pause, the Emperor walks into the next room where day and night a military aide-de-camp, a civil secretary, and two stenographers are at work. There is no jumping up and salut-ing here; a momentary stiffening to an erect position in their respective chairs, and without pause the occupants of this room keep on with their duties. Time-wasting court etiquette is taboo here. The adjoining room is in charge of His Majesty's own personal attendants. One takes the Emperor's helmet; another, with a deft movement, unbuckles his sword; they do this on the run, for the Emperor rarely pauses until he is in his dressing-room. His body attendant awaits him with the *interim* (undress) uniform jacket of a colonel of the First Grenadier Guards. This is a well-worn piece of clothing, comfortably shabby, and the only piece of relaxation which the Emperor permits himself. His Majesty is never seen in dressing gown and slippers. While the Emperor is changing, his body servant hands him a silver basin with a sponge drenched in *eau de cologne,* of which refreshing perfume William II is very fond. It is the only perfume he uses, and is never without; for be it at the theater, at a hunting party, or in the maneuver field, there is always an attendant with *eau de cologne*— of which the Kaiser makes free use. On entering his workroom to the right, the Emperor is handed a short porcelain pipe of an old Germanic pattern, invariably filled with a home product of German tobacco, called *"Knaster."* (Among the many excellent things that Germany manufactures, *Knaster* holds no place.)

The workroom is a dark oak-paneled chamber, upholstered in severely plain olive-green leather.

An enormous oak table, surrounded by six solid armchairs, fills the center of the room. Along the walls, from top to bottom, are bookcases containing every conceivable information on army, navy, law, and administrative matters.

By this time there have assembled in the room men whose business is of such importance as admits of no delay. Always present, is Count Botho von Wedell, the Emperor's chief of the Secret Service. A curt nod, and the Emperor seats himself. Without wasting time on formalities each states his business in a clear and concise manner, often interrupted by sharp, matter-of-fact questions from the Emperor. A short *"Danke, meine Herren"* (Thank you, Gentlemen), they are dismissed, only Wedell remaining. The Emperor presses a button in the arm of his chair and the military aide-de-camp enters, putting down a bundle of papers, which are glanced through. Not a word is spoken. A tap on the table is a sign of dismissal for the aide. Another ring and the civil secretary appears. The same procedure is observed. Not a sound.

The next half hour the Emperor spends in close and absolute privacy with his chief of the Secret Service, and what there occurs no one knows. It is now close on to twelve o'clock. It is at that hour that many mysterious visitors are escorted to the imperial presence, and here, unless the Emperor is in his underground chamber in the Wilhelmstrasse, he instructs his own confidential agents.

The Emperor was in the midst of an emphatic statement, when a note was handed to Count Wedell. Glancing at it, he addressed his master:

"Bertram von Ehrenkrug, Sire, by special appointment."

"Ah, yes, Count. We'll have him in directly. Promising youngster, this. Clever and intelligent. Just the man we need."

After a pause, and as if to himself, "Absolutely dependable; family too closely identified with us, eh, Count?"

Von Wedell acquiesced, but remarked, "But the Truchsess, Sire?"

The Emperor pondered. "H'm; I will take care of that. Have him shown in."

Royalty, although fond of crediting their exalted rank to divine disposition, have found time after time that the feudal aristocracy from whose ranks they originally sprang had more to do with the actual continuance of their power than any divine interference. The mainstay of monarchical power, these free barons, counts, freiherren, lords and dukes, were and are intensely jealous of their privileges. In olden times they fought each other with mutual disaster, as seen in the case of France; to-day both sides find it advisable to protect their mutual interests. This applies especially to semi-absolute countries such as Germany, Austria, and England. In Germany, where all high government positions are invariably held by scions of the old nobility, the prestige of some of them is really tremendous, and although politically the Emperor may and probably would disregard any claims or demands, socially even His Majesty has to be extremely careful in interfering with their respective traditions—traditions in many instances going back a good deal further than his own!

Bertram von Ehrenkrug entered and remained standing at a salute, two paces inside the door, his close-fitting uniform of an officer of the Guard Uhlans setting off his tall, remarkably well-knit frame. The Emperor, after sharply appraising the general appearance of the young officer, returned the salute and, in a pleasant, non-official tone:

"Stand at ease, Ehrenkrug. Come over here," pointing to a spot within two feet of himself. Turning to the Count, who was standing at his right, he commanded: "Begin your examination, Wedell."

"It has pleased His Majesty, Your King, to use you from now on in a private and confidential manner. Your house has served the throne faithfully and well for hundreds of years. The confidence now placed in you is partly due to your family connections, partly to the satisfactory reports received of you. You will have to relinquish your military career, but," with a smile, "from all accounts this will not be any great sacrifice on your part. I have here a report as to your knowledge of languages and other attainments, which I wish to verify. You will answer the questions put to you in the language in which you are addressed."

The Count put his next questions in French, English, and Russian, which were promptly answered in a faultless accent. The Emperor, who had taken up a document, at this point looked up and said:

"Wedell, I am satisfied. I shall leave the rest in your hands."

The Emperor arose, and walking over to von Ehrenkrug, placed his arm on the young man's shoulder, saying:

"Ehrenkrug, I must have men I can trust. You will learn that I have to do many things in an unofficial way, that I have to issue many unofficial orders; that is why I need men of intelligence and integrity. See to it that you do not abuse my need and the trust placed in you. You are from now on my personal messenger, accountable only to me, and in my absence to Count Wedell. Go now to your home and await instructions. You are dismissed."

Retiring to the door, and saluting, Bertram von Ehrenkrug, messenger of the King, went out, embarking on a career, the like of which has fallen to the lot of few men. In after years he was known in the diplomatic circles of a dozen courts as "The Stormy Petrel," for his appearance ever heralded coming troubles.

The already crowded Paris express pulled slowly into the Friedrichstrasse station. A large crowd of Paris-bound passengers made frantic efforts to obtain the remaining seats. A coupé in the center of the train, entirely empty, was the object of quite a number of would-be travelers, who were politely, but firmly, told that this compartment was reserved. A most unusual thing, this, on Prussian state railways, and a good deal of curiosity was expressed; said curiosity being answered by shoulder shrugs of phlegmatic guards and conductors. The train was almost at the point of leaving when a tall young man, his great coat buttoned tightly about him, shouldered his way through the throng, followed by a high railway official. At a sign from the station master, the guards, galvanized into sudden life, sprang and opened the doors of the reserved compartment, and after a whispered conversation between the station master and the head guard, the train was permitted to proceed.

Bertram von Ehrenkrug, for he was the mysterious passenger, made himself comfortable, and leaning back into the luxuriously upholstered cushions, carefully went over his instructions. He felt, naturally, a little concerned at the importance of guarding these well, but their safe delivery was the smallest part of his work. After he had turned over the Emperor's *dossier* to the German Ambassador he was to ascertain

certain things at the Quai d'Orsay, by which one means the diplomatic center of France. The desired information obtained—so his instructions ran—he must proceed at once to Cairo. . . . Cairo! . . . The seat of the English government in Egypt. And as he deciphered the last sheet of his instructions—every page was closely written in code—he seemed amazed at the contents thereof. The stormy petrel was flying before a brewing storm.

Upon his arrival in Paris, Ehrenkrug hired a *fiacre* and was driven to his embassy in the Rue de Lille. After being closeted for a full hour with His Excellency, he hurriedly left the building. His movements during the next hour, had they been observed, would have worried the French secret police. After a visit to the Quai d'Orsay, where Ehrenkrug seemed to know just where to go to get what he wanted, and where, had one been passing down the same dark corridor of a government building, one might have seen a door open and a man, apparently ignoring Ehrenkrug, suddenly hand him a white envelope and rapidly walk away. One might also have seen Ehrenkrug take this envelope without the slightest emotion and after executing some perfunctory business, leave the Quai d'Orsay for the Hotel Anglais. There he hurried through his *dejeuner,* for he must catch the first train for Marseilles. At Marseilles it was a race from the railroad station to the dock.

Aboard the Messageries Maritime steamer *Ville la Ciotat,* bound for New Caledonia, the French penal colony south of Australia, he watched the city of Marseilles disappearing over the stern and smiled a little grimly—or was it not a smile of grim friendliness?—which meant that he was to be a friend to France.

Ehrenkrug had no intention of going to the penal colony, the steamer's destination, and when the *Ciotat* arrived at Port Said, the entrance to the Suez Canal, he disembarked. Learning that the next train for Cairo was not to leave for some hours, Ehrenkrug rambled around.

Port Said has often been described, if a description is possible. The nearest and best description which Bertram had ever read was that of Kipling, but even Kipling's facile pen and lurid portraiture is inadequate to describe this cesspool of humanity. With the exception, perhaps, of Stamboul, Thursday Island, and Vladivostock, Port Said is the most blatantly immoral place on earth. European wickedness is here successfully grafted on Oriental depravity, producing visible results, undreamed of by the most ardent disciple of the poppy. During his stay in Egypt, Bertram learned the devious ways of this Gomorrah rather well, using them to advantage in his future dealings with things Asiatic. . . .

Two men were sitting on the terrace of Shepheard's Hotel in Cairo, the taller of the two easily recognized as Bertram von Ehrenkrug; neither did the other belie his appearance. Monsieur Armand Roneaux was French, distinctly French. From his small, daintily lacquered boots to his coal black, precisely parted hair, he simply exuded Parisian atmosphere. Not an hour ago Ehrenkrug had located this man and handed him the message from the Quai d'Orsay. It had the effect of opening both their confidences, for the matter which they were to discuss was of extreme importance.

Ehrenkrug was interestedly watching the antics of a motley crowd of guides, dragomen and vendors; Mons. Roneaux, twirling his little black mustache, was flirting with a party of rather pretty tourists at a near-by table.

"Diable! Mon cher Comte. We are wasting

good time here. Our good friend is keeping us waiting."

Ehrenkrug, who had noticed his volatile friend's antics, laughingly said: "It's a shame, Roneaux, to miss such opportunities, eh what? But if I'm not mistaken, there's our man," nodding in the direction of a gentleman coming up the main entrance to the terrace. Roneaux gave his companion across the table a searching look, exclaiming, "I thought you did not know him, Ehrenkrug."

"Neither did I, but you gave me a very good description, and I'm rather good at picking men."

The Frenchman arose and signed to the stranger, who, acknowledging the salute of some passers-by, joined their table. Ibraham Mander Bey, for such the newcomer proved to be, was a striking representative of the newer Egyptian generation. His pure Arabian descent was clearly indicated in his fine aquiline features. Well educated, thanks to a paternal British government, he spoke fluent French and English. Since his admittance to the Egyptian bar he had become quite a power in the land, more so by reason of his identifying himself with the rapidly growing revolutionary party.

The Secrets of the Hohenzollerns

It seems that one of the penalties of a somewhat too liberal, broad-minded administration is the ingratitude of the beneficiaries thereof. Men of the Bey's stamp, who but for the generous facilities provided by the British colonial government in Egypt and India, would still, in all probability, remain ignorant fellaheen bakoos, are the first to turn and conspire against the power that raised them. Western education planted in an Eastern mind is often anything but a blessing for both parties concerned, and will some day prove dangerous to the former.

After some cursory conversation, Ibraham Mander Bey invited his two companions to his home to dinner, remarking that his home was a safer place to discuss the weighty matter in hand. Following dinner, served in truly Oriental profusion, the Bey, who made an ideal host, showed his guests into an inner courtyard, just the right sort of place for a secret and undisturbed meeting, there being no windows or lookholes for any possible eavesdropper. Seating his visitors on a couple of luxurious divans, the Bey clapped his hands and ordered the answering *bashi* (servant) to bring *tshibooks* and *mocha,* giving him at the same time strict orders against any interruption. Ehrenkrug, who had spoken very little during the dinner, with true Teutonic abruptness addressed the Bey:

"What is the feeling here as to the proposed move by France in regard to Upper Egypt?"

The rather lengthy reply of Mander Bey did not seem to Ehrenkrug's satisfaction, for it drew from him the somewhat sharp demand:

"Something definite, Bey—let us have something definite. Is there, or is there not, a likelihood of the French project receiving active assistance from your group or the Khedival Party? You know where my government stands. You can rely on the assistance, if necessary, of Stamboul. You have informed the Khedive of the latest developments. What is his attitude? Come now, Bey, let us have a clear understanding. This is your opinion, too, is it not, Monsieur Roneaux?" turning to the Frenchman, who was assiduously drawing at his *hubble-bubble,* evidently quite willing to let von Ehrenkrug conduct affairs. Removing his amber mouthpiece, Roneaux's coinciding opinion was evidenced by an emphatic *"Certainement, certainement,* Monsieur Ehrenkrug."

Having things thus squarely put up to him,

Mander Bey, finding Oriental prevarication of little avail, shrugged his shoulders and replied rather peevishly:

"His Highness, the Khedive, is afraid of Lord Cromer. He is in rather good humor with the British just now, having been granted an additional 200,000 piastres by the Government, besides being infatuated with a beautiful English, or rather American, lady."

"Oh, la, la! *encore une autre! qui est cette belle amie?*" (appreciatively from Roneaux).

"The beautiful Princess Ch——, and oh so wealthy! We will," continued Mander Bey, "have very little assistance from the Khedive. The Party of the Cause is not willing to do anything without the Sheik ul Islam's sanction."

Ehrenkrug, who had been listening attentively, now got up, saying:

"My thanks, Bey, for your frank avowal of the conditions. We expected some such situation," and smiling grimly, "that is why I was sent here. Your reports of the military strength and disposition of the British forces I have forwarded. Many thanks for your hospitality."

After a final glass of sherbet, Ehrenkrug and Roneaux left.

The Secrets of the Hohenzollerns

Slowly wending their way through the narrow, crowded thoroughfares, Roneaux and Ehrenkrug discussed the accuracy of Mander Bey's statement, the Frenchman anxiously inquiring of his companion his version of the affair. "Frankly, Roneaux, Berlin expected some such complication as this. That's why they sent me down here before committing themselves. Without the active assistance of Egypt and Turkey, the French project in the upper reaches of the Nile is doomed to failure, and your magnificent scheme is likely to end in disaster, especially to those entrusted with their execution. However, your government is too deeply involved to pull out now, and it remains to be seen what dimensions the affair will take." He paused and as if to verify something before committing himself to the agent from the Quai d'Orsay, Ehrenkrug drew the momentous sheet of cipher from his pocket. "Monsieur Roneaux," he declared, "I am authorized to assure you that France can absolutely rely upon the political support of Germany in this move. Our Emperor knows that you have not forgotten the lost provinces. He is rather anxious to placate your country. When you move against England down here you can

be assured of his full support." . . . Monsieur
Roneaux seemed immeasurably relieved, and
when Ehrenkrug proposed, "Now let high politics
rest for a while and show me Cairo," Monsieur
Roneaux eagerly assented.

Under the able guidance of his confrère, Ehrenkrug made a pretty thorough exploration of the
Queen of the Nile. There is no other city on
earth where Orient and Occident blend so har-
moniously without destroying their respective in-
dividualities. More Parisian than Algiers,
where, strange to say, one finds all nationalities
but Frenchmen, it is also more truly African than
any other place on the Dark Continent. Here a
magnificent thoroughfare, with up-to-date em-
poriums (prices included); over there, a bazaar
where cobbler and potter make and sell their
wares as they did in the days of the Pharaohs.
On one side the latest invention in electric trac-
tion, alongside of it irrigation efforts, hand-
turned wooden scuppers in use when Moses
showed his magic to the king. The latest crea-
tions of Poiret and Paquin, or the immaculate
Bond Street tailored frock coat, rub shoulders
with yashmak and burnous—truly a city of con-
trasts. Here East and West, Kipling notwith-

standing, meet in more ways than one; yea and intermingle, if the tales one hears from one's dragoman bear one single iota of truth. Fair ladies who would not dream of going unattended to reputable restaurants in New York, London, or Berlin, do not hesitate at all in Cairo to attend séances in places very much the reverse. As there is no reason to doubt the same champagne atmosphere, sparkling and intoxicating, existed in the days of Cleopatra, why blame her over much!

In the year of grace 1901, the situation amongst the leading European powers was more than a little peculiar. England was intensely unpopular just then. She had taken absolute possession of Egypt under the famous ninety-nine year lease clause, much in the same manner and for the same reasons as Germany took possession of Kiao-chau. Through the clever manipulation and far-sightedness of a couple of British statesmen, England had gotten the leading interest in the Suez Canal, the world's greatest highway. Let it be noted here, as usual, much against the will of some of the "old women" at Westminster. It had proved itself to be one of the best, if not the best, investments Great Britain has ever made. Likewise the British control of Egypt was a real blessing to the Egyptian people as a whole, especially the fellaheen. Never since the days of the Pharaohs was Egypt so well governed or prosperous as it is to-day. It does not matter in the slightest by what trickery England gained a hold upon Egypt or some of her other possessions; the fact remains that these countries are immeasurably better off under the Union Jack than they were under a flag of their own.

England's just and benevolent rule, of course, did not suit a certain class of Egyptians who had battened and fattened on the ruthless exploitation of the fellaheen, the common people. The leader of this discontented faction was Arabi Pasha, who cast about for means to start a revolt. He was not long in finding it, for the jealousy of most of the Continental nations of Europe of England's splendid success in Egypt furnished them with the means. It was notably Turkey and France, with quiescent German approval, who used Arabi Pasha as a cat's-paw, and promptly left him in the lurch when their little scheme ended in disaster at Tel-el-Kebir, where the British expedition signally defeated Arabi's forces.[1]

[1] The author met and stayed with Arabi Pasha at Kandy, in Ceylon, the place of his exile, where instead of being shot, he was sent by the lenient British government. In the course of

The Secrets of the Hohenzollerns

Through Kitchener's success at Omdurman, where he crushed the Mahdi, England was enabled to extend her sphere of influence a few thousand miles further south. She promptly declared a protectorate over the whole of the Uganda region much to the chagrin of the other European nations who were casting covetous eyes upon the reaches of the upper Nile.

Italy was still smarting over her defeat by Menelik, Emperor of Abyssinia. She attributed her reverse mostly to England, and with a good deal of reason. The Italian Commander-in-Chief, General Baratieri, with his chief of staff, and Generals Albatone and Dabonnida, were decisively defeated on March 1, 1896, at Adoua by Ras Makonen, the Abyssinian Commander-in-Chief. There is not the slightest doubt that the Abyssinians could never have defeated such able men as the Italian commanders and their heroic troops, but for the totally unexpected up-to-dateness of their equipment. Sixty thousand Martini-Henry and Lee-Enfield rifles of the latest pat-

many conversations the old Arab unburdened himself of incidents that threw strange sidelights on the undercurrents at work in those days in Europe. At some future date the author may be willing to relate some of the confidences of this strange son of the desert.

tern, 3,000,000 rounds of ammunition and twenty machine guns, all of British make, had found their way into Abyssinia. Decidedly, Italy was not friendly to Great Britain. Russia was sticking out her Bear's paw toward the Persian Gulf. Teheran occupied a good deal of time and attention in the House of Commons. No doubt that England was "splendidly isolated." But Lord Kitchener of Khartoum's masterful handling of the Fashoda incident succeeded in making France a friend instead of a dangerous enemy—and the Emperor's scheme that brought Ehrenkrug to Cairo went for naught. Two thousand eight hundred miles inland from Cairo, on the west bank of the Nile, stands Fashoda. The place itself has the usual squalid look and fetid stench of inner African trading stations. But this little-known, insignificant collection of hovels, almost in the center of Africa, was destined to make history.

It was an early July morning in 1898. Three fever-stricken white officers, clad in the loose white tunics of the French Colonial troops, were listlessly lounging in their camp chairs. Outside their open tent a sentry, in the uniform of the French Senegalese, was guarding the Tricolor drooping from a short staff in front. The eldest of the three officers, of medium height, his slight frame attenuated to the last possible degree, was Captain (now Colonel) Marchand, the hero of the unprecedented march across the unknown arid and acrid wastes of the Lower Sahara to this place on the bank of the Nile. For political reasons this phenomenal march of exploration has never received adequate recognition, but if ever a man was entitled to the admiration of his fellow men for unspeakable privations endured, that man was Captain Marchand, his handful of white companions, and his faithful Senegalese.

A black soldier came hurrying toward the tent, and saluting his Captain, breathlessly announced that a large party was entering the east end of the town. The sound of a bugle was heard, and the announced party came into view. At the head of the column rode an officer on a hardy Berber mule. Following him came a half company of Sikhs and a full company of the First Sudanese. At a sign from the officer in front, his company halted and he rode forward. Climbing out of his saddle he walked toward the three Frenchmen, who had risen, and saluting, inquired, "Captain Marchand?" The Captain, returning the salute, bowed.

The remarkably tall British officer held out his hand, saying: "My name is Kitchener. I think we have heard of each other."

Interestedly those two men looked at each other. Both were men of deeds, both had great military achievements behind them. The one in Algeria, Oran, and Morocco, the other in the Sudan and South Africa. In the prime of his splendid manhood, Kitchener's inscrutable bronzed face and steel gray eyes denoted to the full the quiet forceful reserve of his race. He sat erect in his chair, methodically studying the man opposite him. Captain Marchand was leaning back, his legs crossed. An entirely different type physically was this wiry little Frenchman, but notwithstanding his physical discrepancy, the same atmosphere of power and of men who accomplish things was noticeable in one as well in the other. Lord Kitchener made a sign to one of his officers, who handed him a brown leather despatch folder, and taking therefrom an official-looking document, he addressed the French captain:

"The British government, with the understanding and sanction of the Egyptian government, has proclaimed a protectorate over the Sudan, up to a point 110 miles due south of Fashoda.

"Any encroachment upon the indicated territory will consequently be viewed as an act of hostility. My instructions are to prevent such an act of encroachment, or, if actually accomplished, to insist upon the withdrawal of any expeditionary force whatsoever."

Kitchener paused, as if expecting an answer to his statement. Captain Marchand not replying immediately, the British commander continued:

"I am instructed to use force if necessary. As a soldier I shall obey my instructions. I trust that this will be unnecessary. I am a soldier and not a diplomat; but you must see, Captain, that your position is untenable. The British Foreign Office neither could, nor would, permit any foreign power to raise her or their flag over a territory which has justly been proclaimed a British protectorate. I shall leave you the document, signed by His Royal Highness, the Khedive, showing our indisputable right over these regions. You have half an hour in which to make your decision."

The Secrets of the Hohenzollerns

Kitchener rose slowly from his chair, and again holding out his hand to Marchand, who had also risen, said:

"As a brother in arms, and as a man who knows this country, permit me to express my personal admiration of your ability to conduct your party thus far." Saluting, his lordship turned and rejoined his column.

Within twenty minutes, one of the French officers conveyed to the British commander Captain Marchand's willingness to withdraw. It was by this time high noon. A torrid equatorial sun was flaying the poor quaking earth unmercifully. Two lines of soldiers, standing at "Present," were drawn up on either side of the flagstaff in front of Captain Marchand's tent. A command in French, a huge sergeant of the Senegalese Tiraleurs stepped forward, and slowly the Tricolor of France fluttered to the ground. Again a sharp command, a Rasseldar of the Sikhs stepped forward, and the Union Jack of England floated in place of the emblem of France.

At a sign from Lord Kitchener, an officer and a couple of Sudanese, bearing a short flag pole, advanced, and planting the staff alongside the other, bent the French flag on to the halyards.

Kitchener, surrounded by his officers, walked towards the French line. Captain Marchand, divining his purpose, made a sign to his comrades, and advanced also.

It was then that Kitchner showed the wonderful tact—which might have been his, or which might have been inspired by Downing Street—and that was to have far reaching effects.

Under the two flag poles they met. A pull on the running lines, and the flags of England and France floated peacefully, side by side. A very soldierly compliment this, and visibly deeply appreciated by the French officers. It was a peaceful solving of a situation surcharged with ominous possibilities. Almost prophetic, in the advent of latter-day occurrences.

From the desert the news sped with the swiftness of the desert winds to the abode of Ibraham Mander Bey; and hours before the hauling down of the French flag was known in Paris or London it was known in the perfumed courtyard of Ibraham Mander Bey. For only a second did the Arab's eyes betray him as he heard the message that the weary fellah brought; but Ehrenkrug read his disappointment.

Excusing himself Ehrenkrug went to the cable

office; and there followed troubled hours that night in the Royal Palace in Berlin, for the Emperor had believed that against England the sword would be drawn. The cipher report of Ehrenkrug said that the French had almost seemed to welcome the coming of Kitchener, so courteously and with such delicate sentiment had their land been taken from them. Then the Emperor knew that to him Fashoda was a failure, and that instead of the clouds gathering over England they were gathering over him.

He was in his fortieth year now.

CHAPTER V

THE TROUBLE MAKERS

IT is a curious and humiliating truth that after these 2000 years of Christianity and in spite of our much vaunted civilization and progress, the affairs of mankind are often enough directed by anybody but those visible heads of the mightiest nations who claim to have a divinely given right to rule. History, which has a strange trick of repeating itself, has shown in its annals the influence and power of many unscrupulously clever men and women. Cleopatra, Lucretia Borgia, Marquise de Pompadour, or Catherine of Russia, may have no prototypes to-day. True, the age of the *lettres de cachet* and the *oubliette* has gone by. As the adage has it: other times, other manners. But the methods are about the same, despite the passage of years.

As the methods of the medieval robber barons, who lay in wait behind hedges, taking their toll of their fellow men, have changed to the elaborate extraction of the last pound of flesh practised in the modern Wall Street, so have the tactics of the latter-day men and women who play rôles in governments altered from the crude and drastic banquets of death of a Lucretia Borgia to the subtle almost unknown and invisible influence of a Kati Schratt or a Rasputin.

It is a fact, passing strange and almost inexplicable, that the affairs and destinies of the human race are often swayed by these characters who in reality are naught but atoms, obscure, seemingly insignificant, and often uneducated atoms at that. And it is beyond the understanding of even more than ordinarily intelligent people to grasp the possibility of the power and influence of these individuals who exert a force on the whole not dissimilar to that of dark asteroids and stars floating in the solar universe. Much in the same manner as it has been possible for an unknown Irishman from the lower ranks of life to gain political mastery of the second largest city in the world, do these trouble makers gain their sway and become the power behind the throne. When the history of this latest outbreak of insanity in Europe shall have been inscribed in "the big black book of jobs," the names of such men and women as Rasputin, Kati Schratt and Mrs. Keppel will be found recorded there in imperishable letters.

On a somewhat chilly, blustery May afternoon in 1908, the Imperial yacht *Hohenzollern* was met outside Kronstadt in the Gulf of Bothnia by the Tsar's yacht, the *Standart*. The German Emperor was making one of his periodical flying visits to his brother potentate, the purpose of which, having no bearing on this incident, need not be mentioned here. As the younger monarch invariably pays his respects to the elder ruler first, the Tsar's cutter, with the Tsar, Tsarina, the Governor of Kronstadt, and their respective suites drew away from the *Standart* and was soon seen approaching the *Hohenzollern*. In the party there was also one Rasputin.

The cutter of the Tsar was made fast to the royal *fallrep* (companion ladder). It being an iron rule that only persons of royal blood or the commanding admiral of a fleet are allowed to ascend this purple covered stairway, two commissioned officers of the German navy were standing by for the ceremonials. After they had assisted the imperial Russian party from the cutter to the swaying companion ladder, Ehrenkrug saw a thin-faced man in the garb of a cleric attempt to follow. He was Rasputin.

Without a word two German officers locked hands and barred the way. Rasputin pushed forward. Placidly the officers pushed Rasputin back toward the cutter. A sharp command, and it was ordered to proceed to the starboard side of the *Hohenzollern*. Curiously Ehrenkrug watched developments. It was part of his business to know men like Rasputin and their ways. After the imperial suites had been formally introduced and the Kaiser and the Tsar had inspected the guard of honor, Ehrenkrug saw Rasputin climb up the starboard ladder. When he crossed the deck the face of the monk was almost blue-black with rage. In a convulsion, unable to restrain his feelings, he glared at the Kaiser, who was standing eight paces away, chatting to the Tsar. Ehrenkrug unobtrusively drew near the monk and as he did so he heard the Russian say, with a grimace at Wilhelm II:

"Some day you'll pay for this!"

Such is the power of Rasputin, a member of the black monks of the monastery of St. Innocent at Irkutsk. He is an exotic product of that favoritism which can only be seen in its most luxuriant growth in the royal courts of Europe. Of low birth and breeding, he has to the full the Russian peasant's inborn servile shrewdness. A protégé of Pobiedonostef, the late Procurator of the Holy Synod, he attracted, through the influence of his mentor, the attention of the Tsar. It was not long before the Tsar had made Rasputin chaplain of the royal household, and his own private confessor. Thus began his rapid rise to an influential post, a rise that was due to Rasputin's masterful cleverness over the easily influenced Tsar.

To understand this one must understand the Little Father. Nicholas II is one of the most nervous and superstitious men on earth. In continuous fear of Nihilistic attacks, and aware that his court is honeycombed with intrigue, he is thrown into a hysterical state by even such small things as a sudden shadow, or an unaccountable noise. Moreover, his habit of smoking from twenty-four to thirty of the heaviest, black and moist Havana cigars per day has not been conducive to the alleviation of this nervousness. Rasputin, clever charlatan that he is, soon used these weaknesses of his master to his advantage, and it needed only his fortunate manipulation of the illness of the Tsarevitch as a lever to make him the most powerful influence in the court of the Neva.

The Tsarevitch, who from his birth has been a weakling and almost a cripple, was unable to walk. He had always to be carried about by his bodyman, drawn from the Cossacks of the Don, of which he is honorary Hettman, or Chief. None of the eminent scientists who were called in had apparently been able to effect a cure. Rasputin did. Whatever the reason for this cure—whether it was due to Rasputin's knowledge of herbs, gained in his sojourn among the nomadic semi-Asiatic tribes of central Siberia, or the ultimate effect gained by the treatment given by the savants, the fact remains that the lad, under the care of Rasputin, has gained health and strength. This made the Tsarina, whose whole life is bound up in the heir apparent, his devoted patron. And to such an extent did her devotion go that when Rasputin was almost assassinated by a jealous woman on one of his visits to Irkutsk, the Tsarina rushed to his bedside by special train, and personally supervised his nursing. The weapon which was used in the attack is now cherished as a holy ikon, and rests under the Tsarina's pillow.

Thus gathered the tremendous power of Rasputin. From the day he was barred at the royal companionway of the *Hohenzollern* he threw all his power into the scale against Germany and all things Germanic. Previous to his slight at the hands of Wilhelm II, the Teutonic element was fairly predominant in Russian affairs, especially in the commercial and educational branches. Those who know Russia will recall that a few years back the leading banks, commercial institutions, and colleges were generally superintended by Germans. German imports easily totaled sixty per cent. of the whole. This situation soon began to change; gradually the Teutonic element was weeded out from the places of honor and trust, and replaced by Frenchmen and Russians. It was not long before the German secret service chiefs became aware of this changing condition of affairs. All reports and indications pointed directly to Rasputin as prime mover and cause, but despite convincing proofs, the idea of Rasputin influencing the Russian court was promptly pooh-poohed, especially by the

Emperor, a piece of short-sightedness which was to cost him dear.

Similar in form, but different in character, as an almost unknown quantity in forging the destinies of her country was Kati Schratt, the daughter of a well-to-do Viennese merchant. By no means beautiful, although of a charming comeliness; and, by reason of being a thoroughly good woman, very sympathetic, she held sway over Francis Joseph I for almost forty-five years. She was an actress of no mean histrionic ability, and from the moment when the Austrian emperor first saw her in the title rôle of one of Wagner's operas, to this day they have maintained an unbroken friendship. Francis Joseph, singularly unhappy in his domestic relations, no doubt here found sympathetic atmosphere entirely lacking in his own arctic family circle. This remarkably keen intelligence of Madame Schratt was relied upon to a great extent by the ruler of Austria in many personal and national crises, and it is a notorious fact, although little known outside of certain diplomatic circles, that she is invariably consulted by the old emperor.

It is unfortunate for the peace of Europe that

this particular woman, level headed and moderate in most other things of life, was obsessed by an almost insane hatred of all things Servian. An idolized only brother of hers was assassinated in one of the periodical Servian upheavals. The Balkan States, in somewhat similar fashion as do the South American Republics, suffer from a chronic affliction in the shape of revolutionary rashes. More than once during these upheavals have the Servian people had cause to feel the fierce, unrelenting hatred of this woman. It was her doing that the Austrian emperor supported the Bulgarian claims against the Servians in the second Balkan war; it was her doing that the Austrian emperor sent the harsh ultimatum to Servia upon the assassination of the Archduke Frederick and his consort. And it was her influence which prevented many councils of moderation from succeeding with the old emperor. Directly or indirectly, this woman, to the great mass of humanity unknown, was undoubtedly one of the primary factors in precipitating the long threatening European struggle. She was, in short, an unwitting conspirator against the peace of Europe, for Francis Joseph would always listen to her counsels, and they were for war.

The Secrets of the Hohenzollerns

The following is an instance of her influence upon old Francis Joseph.

A hurried summons, and Bertram von Ehrenkrug presented himself at the Royal Palais. For hours the Emperor had been in consultation with his ministers. They had arrived at a decision. Immediate, personal communication must be established with Francis Joseph. With intimate documents, so important that he was told to memorize their contents and destroy them at the slightest menace, Ehrenkrug was despatched to the Hofburg in Vienna. Knowing it is the privilege of the messengers of Wilhelm II to pass unchallenged and without delay into the royal antechambers, von Ehrenkrug, who was known well in the Hofburg, penetrated at once to the Emperor's private domain. Here for the first time in his experience he was stopped. The usher of the inner chamber told him that His Majesty was engaged with Madame Schratt. Well knowing the usual length of these tête-à-têtes, von Ehrenkrug made use of a ruse: approaching close to the door of the royal chamber, he addressed in stentorian tones an imaginary personage: "Important personal messages from His Majesty, Emperor Wilhelm."

As he expected, the old emperor heard the commotion, but, contrary to expectations, it was Kati Schratt who opened the door. "Oh, it is you," exclaimed the lady, who, by the by, had no particular liking for reasons of her own for Bertram von Ehrenkrug.

Thoroughly versed in undercurrent intrigues, he made another bid for the Emperor's attention. "Important messages from His Majesty Emperor Wilhelm."

This time he succeeded in attracting the old sovereign's attention, for he heard a querulous voice exclaiming, "What is it, Kati? Can't we have even one undisturbed hour?"

"Nichts besonderes" (nothing particular). "You are too fatigued just now. This can wait, can it not?"

"Wie du willst . . ." (as you wish), was the old gentleman's tired reply, and the door was closed in the face of the messenger of Wilhelm II.

Not until two hours afterward was Bertram von Ehrenkrug permitted to deliver his documents to the tired old emperor.

There is another class of trouble maker that has no direct connection with high or low diplomacy; it is the friends, *Belles Amies,* or *penchants;* although having no active bearing on the affairs of state these *liaisons* unwittingly, and without the least desire on the part of those concerned, often have far reaching consequences. I have in mind a charming woman of plebeian origin, an American who has gained a wonderful success on the operatic stage. I might mention other decidedly attractive American women coupled with the House of Hohenzollern. My reason for selecting the opera singer, however, is entirely personal. The effect in the ultimate was upon Bertram von Ehrenkrug—a boomerang, as you will see upon the Hohenzollerns.

The association of this lady with the royal house of Hohenzollern is truly an illuminating bit of human document. At the outset, her remarkably able portraiture of the Emperor's favorite heroines attracted His Majesty's attention. It was inevitable that this artist's highly magnetic personality and her calm restful understanding should appeal to the nervous, high-strung temperament of William II. A close platonic *camaraderie* sprung up between these two: platonic, let there be no misunderstanding, in the purest sense of the word; for William II after his ascension to the throne became the most straight-laced Benedict imaginable. No doubt the sweet artistic simplicity of this cultured American girl, untrammeled by court considerations, proved a sufficiently pleasing contrast and relaxation from the stiff and constrained surroundings at his castle. His Majesty used to drop in on No. 20 Thiergartenstrasse, much in the same manner in vogue amongst less exalted mortals. He would be received in a quiet unconventional manner without any fuss whatsoever. There would be present one or two mutual acquaintances, mostly of art circles. The conversation, interspersed with music and singing, was always of a cosmopolitan character, and, after some light refreshments, invariably prepared in chafing-dishes, in the preparation of which His Majesty took a keen interest—with disastrous results if he took a hand in the same!—the Emperor would always be the first to leave.

This idyllic state of affairs received a sudden interruption. The Emperor surprised his own son, the Crown Prince, at the quarters in the Thiergartenstrasse. . . .

His Majesty suffered from one of his restless fits. On such occasions his immediate retinue has got to be prepared for sudden travelings, and this night was no exception to the rule. The Emperor made up his mind for an early morning hunt in one of the well-stocked game preserves of the royal Prussian domain. Soon three motor cars were speeding along the Grosse Alle of the Thiergarten. In the first motor there is invariably one of the Emperor's trusted confidential agents. The next car is occupied by the Emperor and any of his personal friends whom he invites to these parties. The last car contains attendants of the royal household. They were well on the road toward Charlottenburg when the Emperor, in one of his characteristic changes of mood, decided to pay a visit to No. 20. The cars were turned about and soon were traveling along Thiergartenstrasse. The Secret Service agent in the front car recognized a familiar motor car outside the mansion occupied by the lady in question, and foreseeing some serious consequences, made use of the discreet ruse of dashing past the residence. It was his intention to give the parties concerned an opportunity to beat a strategic retreat. But the absence and inattention of the chauffeur frustrated his plan. The cars had gone about two hundred meters past the house when there came a peremptory order from the second car to stop.

"What *zum Teufel* is the meaning of this? Back!"

When eventually the party stopped in front of No. 20, the Emperor immediately recognized the strange car and, without waiting to be announced, stalked past the porter's lodge into the house.

Here occurred a family scene by no means confined to the sphere of ordinary mortals. The Emperor found his son, the Crown Prince Frederick William, evidently very much at home. His temper, at all times easily ignited, there and then gave vent to a volcanic explosion.

"*Du Schafskopf* (muttonhead), what's the meaning of this? What are you doing here?"

"That's no concern of yours," was the rather nonchalant princely answer. It infuriated the old man still further.

And right there history repeated itself. A previous heir apparent to the Prussian throne, Frederick the Great, on a memorable occasion experienced parental wrath in the shape of having his flute on which he was tooting broken over his head. In this instance, the Emperor hauled off and planted a resounding whack on the left side of his son's proboscis. His Royal Highness was placed under arrest by his father and within forty-eight hours took up his duties as a colonel of the famous Death Head Hussars in Danzic. Milady, at about the same time, returned to her own country, where she is still residing.

Witnesses of royal fracases at any time are in a peculiarly dangerous and unthankful position. Bertram von Ehrenkrug, who happened to be the Secret Service agent present on this occasion, experienced to the full the bitter animosity of His Imperial Highness, who without reason, laid the blame for the sudden appearance of his father on Ehrenkrug's shoulders. In the highest stratum of life, Rider Haggard's phrase, "It is not good to know the Thing, too much," gains added significance.

And Bertram von Ehrenkrug is no longer in the secret diplomatic corps of Germany because of this woman; and because of this woman there has been published to the world the things which the world has read of the House of Hohenzollern—which is the author's one reason for disclosing the affair.

The Secrets of the Hohenzollerns

Episodes of this character and description are by no means confined to any individual royal house or government. In all courts and seats of government, with the possible exception of America and Japan, women are still master intriguers, and in no country is this more true than in England and France. The court of St. James has always been more or less petticoat ridden, and it is an open secret in diplomatic circles that in the reign of Edward VII most appointments in the gift of the King were bestowed through the efforts of a number five and a half glove.

Such men as Chamberlain, Lord Kitchener, and Admiral Fisher have all felt the adverse influence of women, for none of these three truly great men has ever been able to truckle or cater to court favorites. Great Britain is indeed fortunate that the ultimate decision lies with her people through the Houses of Parliament; still it is rather deplorable that it requires times of stress and danger such as this present European struggle to bring such men into their own.

Wilhelm II, up to the death of Queen Victoria, was quite the rage in England. As the eldest grandchild of the queen he was much petted by her; but his uncle, Edward, even as Prince of

Wales never had any too much time for his imperial nephew. The Bohemian, easy-going seventh Edward was a shrewd judge of men and horses. His quiet, tactful manner and way of living was directly antagonistic to the Emperor's restless and bombastic personality. It needed only one of the Emperor's periodical outbreaks of more than usual tactlessness to make of his uncle an almost open enemy. Unluckily, the Emperor was not slow in providing just such an occasion.

During the Cowes Week in 1904, the Emperor and King Edward one evening were the guests of honor on Sir Thomas Lipton's yacht. Among the others present was the Hon. Mrs. Keppel. The talk naturally converged about the events of the day, and the Emperor, much elated over the victory of his yacht *Meteor,* bragged a good deal. The Hon. Mrs. Keppel, taking up the cudgels of one of her relations who had commanded one of the defeated vessels, incurred the displeasure of the Emperor by her able witticisms. The unfortunate habit of the Emperor's of talking first and thinking afterwards once again upset the frying pan; for he delivered himself of the following by no means delicate rejoinder: "Huh!

madame, by all accounts you ought to know more about sailors than sails!"

Mortified to tears, the lady rose and with characteristic English dignity withdrew. King Edward, who was talking to Sir Thomas on another part of the deck, had noticed that something displeasing had occurred. On being told the circumstances, he called his nephew into the chart house and evidently gave him an avuncular piece of his mind. At all events, the Kaiser next morning left in a huff. At the time there was much speculation as to the misunderstanding between the two royal houses. This incident, however, is the real cause for the widened breach between King Edward and William II. The Hon. Mrs. Keppel and her clique had a great deal of influence with King Edward and his court. She became an implacable enemy of the Kaiser's. The result of this animosity is felt to this day, for Sir Edward Grey, the Secretary of Foreign Affairs in England, was one of her protégés and in every way he shared her intense hatred of all things German.

Still another instance of how women consciously or unconsciously can become trouble makers is an episode in the career of the Empress

Eugénie. When Ferdinand de Lesseps completed the Suez Canal, the Khedive of Egypt invited all the sovereigns to attend the opening ceremonies. Napoleon III, then in the zenith of his power, sent his wife Eugénie, called the Empress of the French, as his representative. Frederick William, King of Prussia, sent his son, Frederick, the Crown Prince of Prussia, who afterward became Frederick III, Emperor of Germany, as his envoy. Eugénie, who was one of the most beautiful women of her day and at that time at the height of her charm, captivated and in turn was smitten with the Crown Prince of Prussia. They became infatuated to such an extent that even the lax and prodigal Khedive deemed it advisable to abrogate the festivities. On returning to Prussia, the Crown Prince found ways of getting to Paris many times, of course always traveling *incognito*. On one of these occasions, Eugénie, no doubt tired by then of his attention, gave him the cold shoulder.

It was at one of those magnificent semi-private balls at the Tuileries that she refused to dance with the Crown Prince, who for the time being was known as the Comte de Bourg. Somewhat astounded at the sudden change in attitude, the

Crown Prince insisted that she dance. She replied over her shoulder, "Who is the Comte de Bourg that he thinks he can compel the Empress of the French?"

"Comte de Bourg to-night cannot compel anybody," the Prince replied in a passion, "but Frederick of Prussia can and will."

"Alone, monsieur?" came the taunting query.

"No, madame; if need be, at the head of a million men."

Two years after a million German bayonets surrounded Paris. The Crown Prince, up to that time opposed to Bismarck's policy of aggression against France, being rather sympathetic toward that country, over night, however, became a stanch supporter of the Iron Chancellor. And his signal successes in the Franco-Prussian War were one of the main reasons for the quick overthrow of the third Napoleon.

Because another Crown Prince, Frederick Wilhelm, became involved with another woman of France there followed the Zabern incident, when a German officer was inspired to slash a French cobbler with his sword. It happened in the spring of 1914 in a frontier village in Alsace, and it ran through France like wildfire, bringing that old desire for revenge over the "lost provinces" to a white heat. It almost brought war. The Crown Prince wanted war, but the Emperor did not. The Emperor was not ready, besides the Crown Prince was not forty, and history shows that before a Hohenzollern reaches forty he is apt to run amuck. So the Emperor smoothed over the Zabern incident and reprimanded the Crown Prince, who, unlike his famous predecessor of the days of the last Napoleon, is still waiting to march to Paris at the head of a million men. The old, shrewd Teutons who laid down the greatest secret of the Hohenzollerns, that they could not go to war before they were forty, mandated well, for in his calm, mature power, Wilhelm II was biding his time. He was getting ready for the day—there was still much to be done, but when the day did come he would shake Europe as no monarch had ever shaken it before.

CHAPTER VI

THE MASTER HAND

BOOM—boom, boom!

To the somewhat irregular salute of Turkish warships, the Imperial yacht *Hohenzollern,* looking like a white seagull amidst a swarm of grimy and rather unkempt Ottoman war craft, came majestically to an anchor. A gorgeously gilded barge, with priceless Smyrna rugs floating in the water behind, propelled by forty-eight pairs of brawny arms, swept toward the Royal *fallrep.* The oarsmen were clad in spotless white *koumashes,* with scarlet sashes; their head-gear, the *fez,* surmounted by a solid gold tassel. Abdul Hamid, Sultan of Turkey, Padisha of all true believers, was welcoming Wilhelm II, King of Prussia, Emperor of Germany.

As the thunder of the precise return salute of the *Hohenzollern* crashed across the marvelously clear blue Bosphorus, the Sultan with his Grand Vizier and his magnificently attired retinue as-

99

cended to the deck, to be received by the Emperor and his staff.

What a field of study for an anthropologist! On one side, tall, clean-limbed, Viking-like sailors, picked men of the German navy, looking fit in their plain, spotless, serviceable uniform; on the other, undersized, overfed, sickly Orientals, their uniforms all the colors of the rainbow, and smothered in gold lace. On one side, representatives of a virile, hardy, commercial people; on the other, subjects of a decadent, luxuriously somnolent, semi-Asiatic power.

The Emperor, in the neat, full-dress uniform of an admiral, his sun-tanned face alight with virile mentality, made a striking contrast to his under-sized, portly, sleepy-looking, goggle-eyed brother potentate. After the presentation of the Sultan to the Empress, and their respective suites, the cutter of the *Hohenzollern* was smartly piped away, and the royal parties, amidst the renewed salute of guns, left for the Golden Horn, to be received by the most enthusiastic acclamations ever accorded an infidel ruler.

The royal parties landed, and after a grand banquet in the *Seraglio* (the Sultan's palace in Pera) the Empress and her suite returned to the

Hohenzollern. The Emperor and the Sultan went in state to the Grand Moshee (Mosque), harboring some of the most revered relics of Mohammed, and, outside of Mohammed's tomb at Mecca, the chief place of pilgrimage for all true believers. The two monarchs were splendidly mounted on milk-white Arabian stallions of the famous Jhidna breed, with pedigree as long as their tails, the Emperor now wearing the uniform of a Turkish general, even to the red *fez*. Riding slowly through the vast, madly-clamoring throng, they dismounted in front of the Moshee. The deep mellow tones of a large gong were heard, and, dying away, there came the plaintive soul-searching cry of the Muezzins (or Mueddin) perched high above the multitude in the picturesque minarets. *"Allah il Allah-sefka il Mohammed."* Instantly all clamor ceased, and turning their faces towards Mecca, the mass prostrated themselves.

Received by the Sheik el Islam, the Emperor, his boots first covered (at his own request) with slippers, entered the dimly lighted Moshee. A unique incident this: William II, the most powerful Christian monarch of the day, lineal descendant and successor of the very princes who in ages past had fought with all their might the power of the Crescent, walking side by side with the Sultan of all Islam into a Mohammedan Holy of Holies! The Emperor, either out of his deeply ingrained reverence and tolerance for all things religious, or, for reasons of his own, acted so circumspectly that at the end of his visit he was presented with the green scarf of an Hadji, the greatest Turkish token of reverence and esteem, and only permitted to those who have made the pilgrimage to Mecca. This, naturally, has given the Emperor a tremendous hold amongst the Turks, and has more than once been made capital use of, especially in this present struggle, where Turkish troops have been told that the Kaiser has turned Mohammedan. The troops of Turkey, still being largely religious fanatics, are more likely to obey and endure the officers of a supposed true believer than a western *Giaour*.

The spectacular tour of Wilhelm II and his Consort to Turkey and the Holy Land was, at the time, much criticized at home and abroad; nevertheless, it was in reality one of the most deeply thought out, almost genius like coups the Emperor had ever acomplished. Previous to his visit, the predominant power at the Sublime Porte was France. Not alone Turkey, but the whole of the Mussulman countries looked toward France as their chief protector. Later events have shown conclusive proof that France was ousted from this position, the German assuming the rôle of protector-in-chief. The immediate result was a closer political understanding between the Ottoman and German empires, a large influx of German merchandise, the buying of $100,000,000 worth of German war material, the reorganization of the Turkish military system by German Staff officers, and last, but not least, the concession for the much disputed Bagdad railway. It has been said, and with much reason, that the best commercial traveler Germany ever had was the Kaiser himself.

European diplomatic circles were in a turmoil. Conditions were indeed very unsettled. Austria had seized Herzegovina and Bosnia, ignoring Russia's objections and muttered threats, feeling secure in Germany's support. She had every reason for so doing. Wilhelm II had told the Russian Ambassador that he would brook no interference in the Austrian policy of occupation.

Besides, the Kaiser, in his usual dramatic fashion, had publicly announced that he would, if necessary, appear "in shining armor" on the side of Austria. At the time, Russia had to take this rather drastic ultimatum as best she could. Internal troubles, and the serious reverses she had received in the East, left her in no position for active interference. But the humiliation rankled deep, and your Muskovite, true to his semi-Asiatic origin, never forgives nor forgets. This affair was to bear bitter fruit in the future; as yet, Russia bided her time.

The balance of power in Europe had undergone a sudden change. Russia, if not actually feared, was up till then treated with a good deal of circumspection by Germany. The disaster to Russian arms in the Far East and the general internal fiasco, changed this attitude completely. Germany, free from any possible Russian interference, promptly made use of these favorable conditions. The result was the acquisition of the above-mentioned territory by the Dual Monarchy. Unable at this time to back up her opposition by force of arms, Russia cast about for means to regain her lost power and prestige. In the chronic unsettled state of the Balkans she found means ready to her hand. King Alexander I of Serbia was becoming very unpopular in his own country; his own idiotic behavior, and the flagrant indiscretions of Queen Draga by no means endearing him to his people. If anything was wanted to push him off his already tottering throne, his flirting with Austria supplied it. He was not only obnoxious to his own people, but positively dangerous to Russian influence in the Balkans. The Obrenovich had to go.

On the evening of June 10, 1903, a dozen men were sitting in the back room of a squalid ginmill in the Ulitza Skymirz (street of the hill) in Belgrade. The Restaurazia Czarny Pies (Black Dog) was well named, for it looked and smelled like a dog's kennel. Without exaggeration, one could

> "Count two and seventy separate stenches,
> All well defined, and several stinks."

It was a place well chosen for the dark plot about to be hatched. At one end of the rough table sat Nicholai Mashin, Colonel of the Sixth Regiment, an unkempt, bull-necked brute of the bibulous, swashbuckling type of bygone days. On either side of him were three of his officers, of a like ilk, their round bullet-shaped, narrow-bridged heads, close-set eyes and high cheek bones denoting a low, yet cunning, intelligence. A man of quite a different stamp was Lieutenant-Colonel Niglitch, dark, aristocratic, and, but for his coal black sinister eyes, not unpleasant looking. On his right sat one who was evidently his mentor: a suave, smiling, insistent-mannered gentleman, obviously a foreigner, but seemingly very much at home in the various different languages used at this polyglot round table. Basilovitch Semkoff, without doubt, was the most adroit and unscrupulous agent of the Russian government in the Balkans. All excepting Semkoff had been drinking freely, and were talking at the top of their voices. Mashin, who had vainly endeavored to get them to listen, now jumped up and laying hold of a bottle of cognac, smashed it on the table. Amidst a shower of vile epithets he bellowed an order. The noise quieting down, he addressed Niglitch, "Have you received the money?"

"Part of it only," was the reply.

On hearing this, Mashin, his red face instantly taking on a purple tinge, brought his fist down upon the table, and, yelling at Semkoff, demanded to know what the —— that meant.

The Russian blandly informed him that, according to their understanding, the rest of the money would be handed over after the affair was finished. Muttering and growling, Mashin ordered a general meeting at midnight in the barracks of the Sixth regiment. Then shouting wild threats, heedless of listeners, the conspirators dispersed.

Never in all history was a dynasty overthrown by a sorrier-looking crew than this. It speaks volumes for the state in which the Balkans in general, and Serbia in particular, were sunk previous to the Balkan wars. Fate often makes use of queer and brutal tools!

There was much drink, cheap and otherwise, to be had for the asking at the barracks of the Sixth regiment of the Serbian army. It was asked for. Close on the hour of midnight the whole of the 2,000, mostly ignorant loutish soldiers, were in a state fit to do anything their commanding officers might choose to bid. And they were bade.

The royal residence in Belgrade stands on a sloping hill in the east center of the city. Thither the mob hurried. The outer sentries guarding the approaches of the castle, consisting of a half company of this infamous Sixth regiment, carefully and especially chosen, put no obstacle in the way of the drunken party ascending the slope to the royal residence. The inner watch, picked men of the royal bodyguard, were true to their honor, and promptly paid it with their life's blood.

Pandemonium broke loose. With drawn swords and cocked Mauser pistols, the drunken squad hacked and shot their way over the faithful few into the inner chambers of the King and Queen. Whatever is said of Alexander, with or without reason, one thing must be conceded: in the most desperate hour which can befall a human being, he acquitted himself like a man. When the madly inflamed, murderous mob burst into the chamber where he was sitting with Queen Draga, he shielded his wife with true manhood. The Queen, clad in the flimsiest of dishabille, fled, terror-stricken, into a small antechamber. Alexander had dropped his glasses, and, being short-sighted, stupidly stared at the intruders. Although they had come for a definite purpose, with murder in their hearts, such is the ingrained power of constitutional and hereditary authority over even wildly infuriated human emotions, that when he demanded an explanation of this outrageous conduct, the score of assassins had nothing to say.

The King, peering into their faces, recognized Colonel Mashin, and advancing towards him raised his hand. At this moment one of the officers, probably more intoxicated than the rest, fired point blank at his monarch, wounding him in the right cheek. The sight of blood acted on the rest as it would on a pack of wolves. With uplifted swords they advanced on the King, who retreated into the antechamber where Queen Draga was cowering. She was crouching behind a low divan. Two devils in human shape sprang forward and dragging her by the hair across the couch, thrust their swords again and again into her body. At the same instant another cleaved the skull of the King. Every one present stabbed and hacked at these two bleeding figures, all save one, who, refusing to do so, was promptly cut down. Not satisfied with killing their victims, these fiends perpetrated nameless indignities on the poor mutilated bodies and then threw them out of the window. The two mangled forms, once a king and a queen, lay in the courtyard all night until some sorrowing retainers took them into a near-by hovel. History has truly a strange way of repeating herself.

With the elimination of Alexander I, Russian influence in Serbia became all powerful. Russian agents and Russian gold were everywhere. The visit of the Crown Prince of Serbia to Sofia, the Bulgarian capital, engineered by Russia, was a masterstroke of diplomacy. It brought about an active and workable understanding between Bulgaria and Serbia. Only in Rumania did she meet with failure. Vienna and Berlin found it necessary to make a counter move.

A Balkan alliance, under dominance of Russia, was not at all fitting to their scheme of diplomacy. And after the Balkan War, the German Emperor shrewdly estranged Bulgaria and Serbia, precipitating the conflict that weakened all the Balkans.

But to go back: Wilhelm II, like his great ancestor, Frederick the Great, has always shown a distinct penchant for France. This, however, had not prevented the latter from fighting France when he thought it of advantage to do so, and there is no reason to think that the former also would neglect any favorable opportunities. At present, the Kaiser saw fit to make distinct overtures to France, tacitly condoning French expansive movements in Algeria, Tunis, and the French Congo. This attitude, and the growing distrust in England toward Germany, was to bring about an entire change in the European situation. Great Britain, which had been gradually pushed into a "splendid isolation," found this position, if splendid, anything but reassuring.

It was indeed fortunate for England that Edward VII was on the throne. This quiet, Bohemian gentleman, justly named the "King of Tact," knew France and was liked there as no other Englishman or potentate ever had been. Behind the debonnair, easy-going affability of King Edward lay a vast amount of keen penetration and inflexible purpose. It was he who took his imperial nephew's measure, and correctly, as events have proven. On the historic occasion of Emperor Wilhelm II being presented with the freedom of the City of London, King Edward, then Prince of Wales, presided. It was at the famous old Guildhall that the Emperor, just after being presented with the scroll in its golden casket, remarked in a jocular, and somewhat tactless, manner to the Prince of Wales:

"You have made the city free to me. What if

I come and take it?" Quite contrary to his usual tactful toleration of even bad-quality jokes, Edward, Prince of Wales, looking his nephew straight between the eyes, replied:

"Never, my son, if ever I am king."

One fine May morning in 1906, Edward VII, King of Great Britain and Ireland, Emperor of India, quietly crossed the Channel and paid a visit to President Emile Loubet of France. The visit was quiet and unostentatious, no rousing or emphatic speeches being made. King Edward managed to give it the appearance of a joy excursion, and as such it was treated by the courts of Berlin and Vienna, and consequently did not arouse their always uneasy apprehension to any extent. When, however, the French president went on a voyage to the Baltic, and there met the Tsar of Russia, things began to take on quite a different aspect. It soon became evident that an understanding existed between England, France, and Russia; an almost incredible understanding, for had not England enticed and assisted Japan in fighting Russia? Nevertheless, King Edward's master diplomacy gave birth to the Entente Cordiale. The Triple Entente was a *Fait Accomplis*. England's dangerous isolation was a thing of the past. Now began diplomatic intrigue and juggling of a virulent intensity for the mastership of Europe. On one side the Kaiser, Emperor Franz Josef, and Victor Emmanuel; on the other, Edward VII, the President of France, and the Tsar of Russia. The balance of power was too evenly distributed for either side to risk the throw of the iron dice. Hence the efforts of both sides to outdo or outbid each other. . . .

The Emperor's car was racing at even more than its usual speed through the streets of Berlin. Arrived at the Wilhelmstrasse, the German foreign office, His Majesty sprang out of the machine and hastened up the flight of steps leading in to Count von Wedell's chambers. Ushers, clerks, and secretaries slunk out of his path, for the Emperor's close compressed lips and furrowed brow gave an added savage expression to his always stern face. The violent ringing of a bell brought a quaking usher into the Count's study.

"Where's His Excellency? Summon the Count immediately," were the orders shouted at him.

Without noticing his Secret Service Chief's apologies, the Emperor demanded:

"Wedell, where's Ehrenkrug? Have him brought here at once. Also get me Tapken. I want Ehrenkrug to go to Belgrade. I suppose you know what has happened." Without pausing for an answer, the Emperor, banging his fist on the desk, continued:

"They over there" (referring to his Chancellory) "are either badly informed, or are trying to keep me in the dark, but I will know"—still passionately pounding the desk—"what is going on. These murders down there were instigated by some one. You've got to find out by whom. My ever-careful cabinet suggest diplomatic inquiries. What do these amount to? I am in the dark as to what is going on down there, but we'll find out, and then let those who are responsible look to themselves."

The Emperor paused, seating himself heavily in an armchair. Wedell, in the meantime, had quietly transmitted the Emperor's command for the appearance of Ehrenkrug and Tapken. Now he queried, "Where does Your Majesty wish to meet them?"

"Have them here at the usual hour. Wedell, they are trying to isolate me, but we'll see, *Beim Herrgott* (by the Lord God), we'll see."

The Secrets of the Hohenzollerns

The Emperor was on his feet again, walking like a caged tiger up and down the room, muttering to himself, now and again raising his fist. So violent was his temper that even Wedell, accustomed as he was to his master's vagaries, was more than a little alarmed. He, best of all men, knew what this human dynamo was capable of doing. This single human being, acknowledging responsibility only to himself and God, on moments like these even relegating the Deity into a temporary background, was a terrible factor, not only in the lives of his sixty million subjects, but of the whole of Europe. Firmly believing in the destiny of his country to be the leading nation of Europe, he held an equally firm belief in his destined mastership, for was he not War Lord of Europe? But there were obstacles in the way. So far, all was tranquillity. No *Agadir* incident had occurred, and the fateful journey of the Austrian heir apparent and his wife was yet to be made. But low down on the edge of the horizon, dark and sinister clouds were banking, and intermittent forks of lightning were cleaving the black, forbidding mass.

Who was to be Master of Europe? The answer is buried deep in the bowels of Fate.

CHAPTER VII

THE COUNT OF HOHENECK

AFTER the Emperor's success in compelling the retirement of M. Th. Delcassé, thus removing for the time being the strongest anti-Germanic influence in France, His Majesty thought this an opportune time to make a strong bid for the approbation of the French public. Forthwith Frenchmen of letters, journalists, litterateurs and artists were invited, cordially received, and lavishly entertained in Germany. The Emperor spent large sums out of his private *schatulle* for the production of German, especially Wagnerian, operas and dramas in Paris. French women, *Dames du Salon,* idolized leading actresses and the queens of the demimonde were cleverly won over to assist a general Germanic propaganda. That the inborn tact and finesse of these French women still play a great rôle in the public life of France, is nowhere more clearly understood than at the Wilhelmstrasse. Clean-

116

cut officers of aristocratic crack guard regiments were given furlough in batches. In many cases when their own private means proved insufficient, their purses were lengthened and strengthened in an unusually generous manner by the Wilhelmstrasse. The only stipulation as to the duration of stay or the expenditure of money was that the same must be spent in Paris or the fashionable watering places of France. Paris soon swarmed with Prussian officers in mufti. To an onlooker it was an amusing sight to see the dainty petitely svelt Parisienne escorted by the easily distinguished Prussian guardsmen. More amusing still it was to watch the disgusted comically ferocious expression and twirling of mustaches of the *boulevardiers* and *flaneurs*. Taking it by and large, the Emperor's clever scheme promised "to get across."

The French Cabinet, which was suffering from one of its perennial internal dissensions, was still further undermined by the manipulations of the Wilhelmstrasse. The ever-present royalist party and movement in French politics were cautiously nursed along. The whole situation was ripe for a *coup d'état*. But for the hair-brained, headlong impetuosity of The Orleans there might have been floating to-day the Fleur de Lis instead of the tricolor over the Tuileries.

But William II was quite alone in this effort to win the sympathy of his neighbor to the west. There were influences in his own court circle and family that strongly opposed anything French. They looked for a final subjugation; he looked for a strengthening of friendly relations through which his will would be exerted to attain those aims of influence and power. That the task devolved upon him and him alone will shortly be seen. . . .

Three men were toiling up one of the steep crags of the Tyrolean Alps. They were after chamois, the king of European game, and they were hunting in the Fürst zu Fürstenburg game preserves, noted for its abundance in chamois. Arriving on a little plateau overlooking and giving a clear view of the valley beneath, their *Alpensteiger* called a halt, and opening their Rucksacks, they began munching their luncheon. Their sport had evidently been successful for the two hunters proudly displayed two fine *Gemsbärte* (the brush under the chin of a chamois) on their Tyrolese hats.

Far down the valley a shot rang out. After a tense scrutiny of the pass below, their keen-sighted guide announced that the firer of the shot was a Fürstenburg retainer, evidently trying to locate them.

"Lend me your glasses, Ehrenkrug."

Clapping the hunting binoculars to his eyes, young Wolfgang zu Fürstenburg exclaimed, *"Donnerwetter!* He's right! I wonder what's up."

Ehrenkrug, who was stretched out full length on the soft green moss, lazily rolled over, saying, "Why bother? If he doesn't find us we needn't worry."

Two more shots rang out and a white handkerchief was waved down below.

"Zum Teufel auch, it's too late. He's seen us now."

Picking up his *Pirschbüchse* (a long hunting gun used especially for chamois) he fired an answering shot. Idly speculating what the sending of a special messenger into this wilderness might mean, they awaited his arrival.

After a toilsome climb the breathless messenger handed Bertram von Ehrenkrug a stout blue envelope with "Urgent" written on it in red ink.

As soon as Ehrenkrug clapped eyes on the missive, he became galvanized into action, and with a muttered "Damn, they'll find you even in Hell," tore it open.

The disgusted look on Bertram's face made his friend laughingly exclaim, "Oh ho! *Alter Junge,* the Stormy Petrel is off again!"

"You're right, old man—off with a vengeance," was the curt rejoinder.

Knowing from past experience the futility of questioning his close-lipped friend, young Fürstenburg with a resigned, "That comes from having mysteriously important friends!" gave orders to pack up.

Forty-eight hours afterwards Bertram von Ehrenkrug was quietly shown into Count von Wedell's private chamber.

"Sorry, Ehrenkrug, to curtail your vacation, but you had at least a couple of weeks of relaxation and comparative freedom of action. I have not had a week in years. I have sent for you because something of the utmost importance is under foot. It is so important that the Emperor is going to undertake the thing in person. I want you to accompany the Emperor. His Majesty intends to . . ." here the Count leaned over to

Ehrenkrug and whispered something in his ear.

Ehrenkrug, accustomed as he was to the suddenness and vagaries of His Imperial Master, could not suppress a nervous start. "Impossible, Excellency! Can't be done. His absence is bound to be noticed. And what about a possible recognition? I won't be responsible for his safety."

"Be quiet. The responsibility is not yours, but ours. Do not trouble your head about his absence here or his recognition there. What you have got to do is to obey orders—put your knowledge of ways and means at our disposal, and do your best in safeguarding his person. You will find here the whole plans carefully written out," continued the Count, handing Ehrenkrug some papers. "Commit them to memory and burn them. From here to the border we will find no difficulty at all. It is only after leaving Metz that we will have to exert and to rely more or less on our own resources."

Ehrenkrug, who had listened with ill-concealed agitation, now sprang up saying, "I must respectfully and firmly decline this mission. The responsibility, notwithstanding your declaration, is still too great. For myself," shrugging his shoulders, "you know, Count, I don't care a hang. But to be responsible for the Kaiser's person, no. That's more than you can ask of any one, especially me. So again, Excellency, you will have to excuse me."

Graf Wedell had listened patiently to Ehrenkrug's tirade, and smiled quietly. "Sit down, Ehrenkrug. You're old enough now and you have been long enough with us to know that we never do anything without sufficient reason and without weighing every possible consequence. If your Kaiser sees fit to do a thing, it is not for you to question. I myself have pointed out to him the danger, but you know our master well enough to know the futility of trying to persuade him to desist from anything that he has made his mind up to do, especially where his own person is concerned. The Emperor is convinced that this is necessary and any backing out would stamp him a coward in his own eyes. And *you* know the Emperor's total absence of physical fear. I am telling you all this, Ehrenkrug, for I understand and appreciate your agitation. You know that I am not in the habit of giving explanations and that you have no right to them. Yours is to obey, not to question. Let this be realized. Because of the unusual circumstance, I departed from our rules. Now master your instructions and get ready. We will leave to-morrow evening at eight o'clock."

Ehrenkrug, who had sufficient time during the rather lengthy tirade to compose himself, got up from his chair with deliberation. He slowly put on his gloves. When they fitted to his entire satisfaction, he looked up and addressed the Count, who was keenly watching the set and stony expression on von Ehrenkrug's face. "Your Excellency, nothing you have said or could say will make me undertake this mission. I know the consequences of disobedience. I will take these consequences. If you have no further orders, will Your Excellency permit me to retire?"

Receiving a curt nod from the Count, who was still closely scrutinizing the young man's face, Bertram von Ehrenkrug clicked his heels and left.

Graf Botho von Wedell, Privy Councilor to His Majesty, and Chief of the Emperor's Secret Service, remained sitting in front of his desk staring in a brown study out over the Wilhelmplatz. "Hum! I don't know if I blame the lad over much. Don't know but what I'd also refuse, if the circumstances were reversed. Wonder how the old man will take this? Likely to break Ehrenkrug, though. A thousand pities."

At that moment a tiny bell began tinkling on the Count's desk and a red disc appeared on a small box-like instrument at the side of the writing table. This was the sign that the Emperor had returned to his residence in Berlin and indicated a wish on the part of the Emperor to get into communication with the Count. All the principal service chiefs, as well as the chiefs of the General Staff, the Admiral Staff and the Heads of the Police have these indicators in their offices and in their private homes. The Emperor is thus enabled to get into immediate personal touch with the various heads of his departments. The switch boards are operated from the royal palace and are entirely independent from the general telephone and telegraph service. A special insulating device is used which prevents any possibility of wire tapping. Over these wires the Emperor can and does hold conversations with his ministers of the utmost confidential nature and importance without the least likelihood of any eavesdropping.

The Count took up the special receiver. "No. 1. *Zu Befehl!*" (At orders!)[1]

The Emperor was evidently asking about the progress made in perfecting the plans for his intended journey, for the Count reported Ehrenkrug's refusal to have anything to do with the undertaking. Receiving some peremptory commands, the Count replied, "Useless, Sire. He had that typically Ehrenkrug mule expression on his face, and I know the breed too well. To try persuasion and force is of course out of the question. . . . You command Ehrenkrug's presence? *Zu Befehl,* Sire."

That afternoon Ehrenkrug received a summons to attend the Emperor at the close of the gala opera. Punctually at quarter to eleven Ehrenkrug presented himself to the usher at the royal box and was told to wait and accompany His Majesty to his chambers at the Wilhelmstrasse. At the close of the performance the Emperor took leave of the Empress and his family; and at a sign, Ehrenkrug entered the second of the two waiting royal motor cars, which were driven rapidly to the Wilhelmstrasse.

[1] It is an invariable rule that all secret service officials in communicating with the Emperor or each other always use a number, the Emperor replying with the letters "S.M."

The Secrets of the Hohenzollerns

Here in the famous underground chamber [1] Count Wedell awaited His Majesty. Without pause the Emperor walked into the inner chamber, Ehrenkrug remaining in the outer room. An officer in the undress uniform of the First Royal Life Guards was guarding the door. Ehrenkrug had to wait fully a half hour before summoned to the Emperor's presence. During this time, although both young men, the officer and Ehrenkrug, were well known to each other, both being scions of old noble houses, not one word of conversation passed between them. Such is the ironclad rule of the Emperor's personal staff.

The inner door opened and Count Wedell beckoned Ehrenkrug into the inner chamber. The Kaiser was sitting at his historic green baize-covered writing desk. On Ehrenkrug's entrance, he glanced up from some plans he was perusing and pointed to a spot within a few feet of his seat. *"Komme hier."*

Ehrenkrug advanced. Slowly the Emperor looked him up and down, at last fastening his eyes on Ehrenkrug's face. When closely scrutinizing another person, the Emperor has a trick

[1] A description of this chamber is included in *The Secrets of the German War Office,* in "The Kaiser Prevents a War."

of slowly screwing up and opening his eyes, producing a rather startling effect upon most persons by reason of the penetrating clearness of his large steel grayish-blue eyes. Ehrenkrug stood his scrutiny well.

"So, the Freiherr von Ehrenkrug is not willing to undertake the bidding of his Emperor," the Kaiser began calmly. "The Freiherr von Ehrenkrug, aged twenty-nine, presumes to criticize the action of his liege master." The Emperor's voice began to be strident. "Let me tell the Freiherr von Ehrenkrug that without his addition there are quite enough jackanapes who think too much but do not act enough." The Emperor was pounding the table by now. "But, *Beim Ann-herrn* (by my ancestors), I will teach them a different tune. Obedience I want, not advice! Understand?"

Ehrenkrug, who had stood motionless during the Emperor's tirade, simply lifted his hand to the salute.

"Speak up! What's the reason of your refusal to Count Wedell's behest?"

Ehrenkrug still stood like a stone figure.

"*Schockschwerenot!* Are you dumb? Answer."

After swallowing hard a couple of times, Ehrenkrug, rather red in the face, broke out bluntly, "I refuse, Sire, because it is an absolutely foolhardy proposition. And," Ehrenkrug, getting warm, continued, "if none of Your Majesty's advisers has the courage to say so, I will take it upon myself to point this out. I know the risk and danger and the possible consequences better than your stay-at-home old fossils. I will not be party to a scheme which has ninety-nine out of a hundred chances of endangering Your Majesty's life. I have risked my own willingly and without hesitation in your service, as my forebears did before me, but this I will not do."

The Emperor, who had been keenly watching Ehrenkrug, leaned back in his chair and in an altered tone of voice said quietly, "Listen, my son, Your Kaiser will tell you something.

"I have a duty to perform toward my people, my country and my dynasty. But I am prepared for others not to understand it, and to contest. Duty, my son, you must not forget is entirely different for certain individuals and shaped according to their position and station in life. My duty is not yours and vice versa."

The Emperor paused, and shifting his position

so as to take Count Wedell into his range of vision, he continued, "Have you ever given it a thought, Wedell, that my grandfather on his death had not quite achieved the task which he set out to perform? That, although he renewed in his person the glory and tradition of the old Germanic Empire, yet he had not entirely lived up to them? It was all fine and well to have been proclaimed Emperor of Germany at Versailles, but it was not enough. Look at our position from a geographical point of view. We are surrounded by enemies, without the vital necessity of outlets to the seas, save where we artificially created them. Through the congestion in the few ports we have we are beginning to suffer from acute arterio-sclerosis.[1] The pulse of the people cannot get through. Can we under circumstances such as these play the dominant part we ought to in the destinies of the world? I have been reproached for militarism, but the moment I give up this power we lose all our advantages gained through the great wars of my ancestors and my grandfather who created the new Germany."

[1] The Emperor is very fond of using scientific, especially medical terms in his conversation.

The Emperor paused again. Taking his hand he stroked his forehead with a weary gesture, then almost to himself, "But we cannot go on forever in this defensive position we occupy to-day. I cannot do so because this is already misconstrued. In order to silence my enemies and stop the tongues of our detractors, I must make a final effort. Do not misconstrue my words. I do not harbor sinister designs against my neighbors, but I am getting older and I cannot help thinking more deeply than I have ever done before on the future that awaits Germany and my dynasty. I have become a grandfather, and it is but natural that the future of my grandchildren preoccupies me. As long as I am here all may be well, but can you assure me that it will be so when I am dead? My ancestors and I have followed closely the rules and traditions of our house, but there have been mighty changes, and my son may not follow as closely along the same lines as we have done unless I leave him an inheritance so firmly established that nothing can wrest it from him. I am not thinking of war. My youthful ardor has long since gone. When I looked upon war as glorious in the years gone by, influence of which you know nothing prevented me. Now, I would take the sword only as a last resort. But I have kept ready. The question arises, whether I can keep on being ready forever. The sacrifices I have made are known only to me. I will make one more, and only one." The Emperor had gradually worked himself into one of his passions—"And, by the God of my *Annherrn,* let those who oppose me look to themselves. Time and time again I have *verschluckt* (swallowed) sneers and insults for the sake of my country and because the time was not ripe, but . . ." Here the Emperor made one of his characteristic gestures with his right arm. "Enough!

"Ehrenkrug, your Emperor demands and you will obey. Wedell, I want to be left alone."

Three days later the papers of Berlin informed the public that His Majesty was going to enjoy a short week of hunting at Rominten. The usual crowd of curious onlookers was waiting outside the *Lehrter Bahnhof* to watch the departure of the Kaiser. The royal carriage deposited the Kaiser and some Court-charges in full view of the hurrahing multitude. Recognizing their acclamations, the royal party boarded the imperial train which promptly pulled out of the station.

The Secrets of the Hohenzollerns

His Majesty William II was apparently off for one of his famous hunting trips.

About the same time at a little side entrance on the *Pariser Bahnhof* a taximeter deposited three men who went immediately into the station master's private room. No one saw them enter, for the whole platform was deserted. An express engine coupled to a first class day coach was backed into a siding. The shortest of the three men, who wore a large black velour hat much affected by artists of the Quartier Latin, pulled well over his eyes, was hiding his right arm under a green checkered traveling plaid. They boarded the waiting train. Quietly engine and coach slid out into the night.

At Frankfort-on-the-Main the carriage was unobtrusively shunted onto the Berlin-Paris express. On the Grenz-Station (border station) a keen observer would have noticed that neither the German authorities nor—and this was stranger still—the French officials went near or bothered in the slightest degree the three occupants of that particular carriage.

Arrived at Paris, the trio leisurely descended from their coupé and mingled with the throng of

132

incoming and outgoing passengers. At the Grande Portal they were met by a gentleman dressed in the conventional Parisian attire—a frock coat, muffler and high hat—who merely lifting his hat, beckoned them to follow him. Entering two waiting fiacres the party was driven to a small hostelry, the Cœur d'Or, in the Rue de la Paix.

In a small dingy back room parlor of this third rate Parisian hotel two men were awaiting the arrival of this mysterious party. The elder of the two was walking restlessly up and down the narrow confines of the room repeatedly ejaculating, "They ought to be here by now. I wonder why Wedell insisted on my meeting his companion. Is it possible that it can be the . . . Pshaw! Impossible. Even he wouldn't dare take the risk."

"What's the use of worrying? We'll soon know who it is. In fact, I think they are here now. I can hear some one in the adjoining rooms."

He had hardly finished speaking when the door opened and Count Wedell entered the room. Carefully closing the door, he walked with outstretched hand toward the elder of the two men, saying, "I am very glad to find you waiting for us. He" . . . Wedell whispered something into his companion's ear . . . "does not like to be kept waiting."

The Frenchman, who had jumped back with a startled exclamation, *"Grand Dieu, c'est impossible,"* sank limply into a chair, staring vacantly into Wedell's face. Drawing his hand with a weary gesture across his forehead, he almost whispered, "What a terrible risk for all of us. What if he should be recognized! What if this becomes known! Count, do you know that this is extremely unfair to me? I would never have been here had I known whom I was to meet."

"Calm yourself. We have eliminated all possible risks. In any case," continued the Count, grimly smiling, "it is too late now. As to being unfair to you, that may be so, but your very admission proves to me his correctness in insisting that the identity of your visitor should be kept secret until the last moment. Are you ready? Well, let us go and see him."

The Count walked toward the door. Turning around to the hesitating and evidently still perturbed gentleman, he said, "Why this hesitation? You know that you have got to go through with it now. It is unnecessary for me, is it not, to point out to you why?"

With a helpless gesture, the man in the chair got up and prepared to follow the Count, signing to his silent companion to accompany him. The Count, on observing this, turned again and crossing his arms said this time in a distinctly harsh tone of voice, "No third party, if you please. Monsieur" [1]—making a curt bow to the younger of the men—"is, of course, known to me, but his presence is out of the question. You will please content yourself with remaining and guarding the outer room. Ehrenkrug will remain with you."

The Count opened the door, and motioning the gentleman to proceed, stepped into the next room, closing and locking the door behind him.

The shortest of the three men who had left Berlin the previous evening was half reclining on a rickety sofa. On the entrance of the Count and his companion, he pulled himself into an erect position. Wedell stepped forward saying, "Count Hoheneck, permit me to present Monsieur Joseph Caillaux."

---

[1] Certain unavoidable reasons compel the author to withhold the name of the third party present. He was a member of the French diplomatic corps at the time who has since retired but is still alive.

The Frenchman, who was soon after to become Prime Minister of France, stepped forward and making a deep obeisance, said, ". . . Your Majesty—"

"My dear Caillaux, I prefer to be known as the Count of Hoheneck," replied the personage sitting on the sofa. "Come and sit here beside me. Count, you get yourself a chair."

In this dingy back parlor William II, Joseph Caillaux and Count Botho von Wedell were closeted for more than two hours. At the end of this time Caillaux quietly left the hotel by a side entrance.

That evening the Count of Hoheneck, contrary to the succinct advice of Count Wedell and the fervid pleading of M. Caillaux, insisted on seeing something of Paris by night. In the Bal Tabarin, one of the places visited, the Count Hoheneck, notwithstanding his very excellent disguise —the Kaiser's hair was dyed and his mustache waxed in the French fashion down to a point— was recognized by a staff reporter of *The Figaro*, who promptly traced the Emperor to his place of residence and through clever investigation found out that M. Caillaux had also been seen leaving this particular hotel. The accidental recognition of the Emperor by this reporter resulted in the death of M. Calmette a few years later, an incident that will go down in annals as one of the most interesting crimes—from the point of world politics—ever committed.

Calmette was manager of *The Figaro* and the news being carried to him, promptly silenced the mouth of his reporter, storing this information for future use. On Caillaux' becoming Prime Minister of France, Calmette, no doubt, made capital out of his possession of this secret. His earlier influence with Caillaux was notorious, and the subject of a good deal of speculation.

Finally there came a time when the extortionate demands of Calmette, especially the latter's advances as regards Madame Caillaux, were met by refusals. Then began Calmette's threats. Caillaux had informed the German Secret Service of Calmette's knowledge of the Emperor's visit to Paris and of his consequent dangerous position. Two distinct attempts by German Secret Service employees were made to procure the silence of Calmette, one way or another. In the first instance the sum of half a million francs in cash was accepted by Calmette. But Calmette was not satisfied with purely pecuniary advantages. He soon began to use again his knowledge as a lever. Realizing the impossibility of obtaining absolute guarantees of Calmette's silence, Count Wedell hit upon the Machiavellian plan of using Madame Caillaux in removing this dangerous antagonist —dangerous in more ways than one.

Through his general fondness for women and particularly his known infatuation for Madame Caillaux, Calmette left himself peculiarly open to an attack of this sort. The ever-growing and bitter antagonism of Calmette toward Caillaux and the former's broad threats and hints of his power and ability to vitally injure her husband were cleverly used by German Secret Service emissaries to instil in Madame Caillaux a frenzied hatred of her husband's detractor. Calmette's ruthless methods in using the past history of women as stepping stones for personal and political aggrandizement made the subsequent attack on his life a very logical one and removed it far enough from the real cause to avert suspicion. Calmette, for reasons of his own, had let it become apparent that his exposures would come through Madame Caillaux! This was immediately fastened on to by German Secret Service agents who imbued this unfortunate lady, already brooding, still further with the idea that she alone could save her husband. It is an easy matter to drive a woman of Madame Caillaux' devotional temperament to extremes. The consequence is well known. She went to the directeur's office and calmly shot him down. In a subsequent trial she was acquitted, not so much through the reason of public sentiment as through the disinclination of the French government to stir up poisonous ashes. The time was too super-charged with danger for the Government to risk a far-reaching scandal that would probably have resulted in the total disruption of the French Cabinet. Quietly, but insistently, they went about and eliminated the danger spot out of the French public life. . . .

As quietly as the party had left, so they re-entered Berlin. The next morning the populace acclaimed the real, instead of the pseudo, Emperor.

He had accomplished his task—accomplished it practically single handed, accomplished it without the knowledge of his foes. How this was done and how he has been able to undertake such a daring coup is easily explained.

Authentic, yet conflicting rumors of the Emperor's being seen and observed in certain localities from time to time have puzzled diplomatic cabinets and especially newspaper men a great deal. There was, for instance, the Kaiser's sudden visit to the Emperor of Austria in 1906. Although engineered with painstaking secrecy, through some means or other, a clever correspondent of *The Temps* of Paris ascertained the Emperor's presence at Ischle, a favorite countryseat of Francis Joseph. He informed his paper of this startling occurrence and promptly the cabinets of Europe, always uneasy in regard to William the Sudden's movements, became furiously agitated. Rumors and editorials embarrassing to Germany appeared immediately but were quickly extinguished by emphatic cables from all the foreign correspondents of the world's papers in Berlin who had seen the Emperor in person driving at the time in question in an open carriage in Unter den Linden and attending a performance of the royal opera. Nevertheless, His Majesty was really at Ischle. On this, as well as other occasions, one of the Kaiser's two substitutes impersonated him. These two men are selected for their close resemblance to the Emperor; one especially, an ex-actor, is able to portray the Kaiser with such minute exactness that he more than once has startled and dumbfounded even the immediate entourage of the Kaiser, much to the latter's amusement.

CHAPTER VIII

ENGLAND'S MENACE

THE moon on the night of October 7, 1910, was surrounded by a slender hoop of weird, ghostly, greenish-yellow light, as if a fiend had placed a halo there. Great marching masses of distorted, storm-driven clouds slowly moved across the grisly heavens, as if to shut out something that was to transpire below. It was a night of ghosts; the gray-cloaked figures might have been ghosts. They glided around a long, low iron structure, the seaward end of which gaped wide, and their voices when they gave their terse orders were but penetrating whispers.

On the road from Swinemunde, the seaport for Stettin, to the outer mole the sentries had been tripled. Extra alert and swift, they compelled all traffic to return or make a wide detour. Up this road a motor car was swiftly approaching. The sentry saw that it contained five well-cloaked passengers. Springing to the center of the road, he challenged; a single order from the man in front and the sentry gaped. Then discipline urging him, he stiffened to attention. The car proceeded. It drove swiftly toward the big black shape that opened on the sea. At the entrance of the structure it stopped; expectantly the five men leaned forward. As if but awaiting their arrival, there crept soundlessly out of the enclosure, a silvery, cigar-shaped form, swaying slightly, one almost thought chilled by the autumn night; it was fully exposed to view.

"Sinister."

Involuntarily the word fell from the youngest of the men in the car.

They were watching what might have been a gigantic whale that seemed to hang in the air six feet from the ground, suspended as if by levitation. At once two of the occupants of the car, younger than the others, saluted their companions and walked toward this strange monster. The two men who were left in the automobile watched them swiftly ascend a short iron ladder that dangled from the monster's belly and then grotesquely withdrew into its interior. They heard almost immediately a soft droning; they saw the huge shape quiver an instant, then its nose pointed

upwards at a sharp angle and the thing majestically mounted into the night and rapidly disappeared from sight. The two men in the car had
watched in utter silence, but as the strange object faded into the eerie sky the larger of the two
men stood up. Raising his hand in the salute he
said: "Your Majesty, I have kept my word."

The Emperor, his face still turned to the midnight sky, held out his hand, saying simply, "The
Fatherland's thanks are due to you, Count."

Thus did Wilhelm II and Graf von Zeppelin
watch the trial flights of the first dreadnought of
the air.

The great Zeppelin hurtled through space; but
von Ehrenkrug gave no thought to its speed, so
easily did the ship ride. From the moment he
had left the upper motor, however, von Ehrenkrug began to have a surfeit of new emotions.
As he climbed up the dangling ladder and made
his way toward the pilot and observer in the forward conning tower of the airship, the novelty
of his observations had enthralled him. And
now, as the great craft swam steadily and noise-
lessly up into the night, he heard no sound but the
voices of his companions, for the motors of the
great ship turned in silence. Three thousand

feet below he could see where the land left off and the water began. Accented by the exaggeration of color that such height gives, the edge of the Baltic rimmed the land in hazy, silvery gray. They were heading straight out to sea. No longer were the uncertain shadows of the earth visible. Somewhere down in the vast void through which they coursed there seemed to float a shimmering haze of unearthly light, as though the heavens were flooring the night with celestial silver. Down there a whistle hooted; steadily they flew on.

The commandant suggested, as they had still two hours of flight before reaching the Swedish coast, a tour around his vessel, which Ehrenkrug readily accepted. Starting from the conning tower they went along a well-lit companion-way leading into a comfortable mess room. Another short passage, and the commandant pointed out two doors on either side, one of which he opened, and which led into a small semi-circular room protruding like a swallow's nest from the inside of the Zeppelin. This was a torpedo room, bare at present, but carrying, when on active service, six 50-pound aerial torpedoes. Next he was shown one of the two machine rooms where a

200-horse-power, almost silent, Diesel motor supplied the power for two of the four aerial propellers. Adjoining was the electrical appliance chamber, containing dynamo and huge batteries for the wireless service. The whole interior of the ship was a marvel of well-thought-out compactness.

Ehrenkrug was told that besides a crew of twelve, they carried ballast to the tune of two and one-half tons. Next they ascended two short flights of iron stairway, leading right into the interior of the gas envelope. Here Ehrenkrug counted twenty-six separate compartments, twelve to a side, and one at each end, each containing an independent balloon. Noticing a number of small steel cylinders, he asked what they were, and was told that they contained the lifting power of the Zeppelin. Ascending still higher, and climbing through a trap door, they stood on a wind-swept upper or hurricane deck. In the middle was a short mast, with its spider-like antennæ: the aerial receiver. In the bow and stern were two gun platforms, intended for quick-firers, also two squat structures, which proved to be powerful searchlights.

Just then an orderly, putting his head through

the trap door, announced that the Swedish coast was in sight, and they returned to the conning tower, where the observer pointed to a dim outline far ahead. Glancing at the aerostat, and finding 3,000 feet of an altitude, the commandant gave an order for an elevation of 4,000 feet. The pilot manipulated various levers and instantly the floor of the Zeppelin began to slope, coming to an even keel when the desired height was reached. They were now well within the cloud line, their desired object, for, as the commandant remarked, grimly smiling, "We are no ways keen on being seen."

The observer was busy leaning over his compass and chart, and presently announced that they were over Swedenbourg, a distance of 480 kilometers from Swinemunde. From there they cruised over Upsala, the famous old Swedish university town, when the pilot, receiving an order, turned the nose of the Zeppelin homeward.

The landing, after an eighteen hours' flight, in which more than 1,300 kilometers (about 850 miles) were covered, was accomplished without mishap. The same silent, gray-clad figures received the vessel. The crew immediately left by motor cars, only the commandant, Ehrenkrug, and the observation officer remaining. A sharp order to the foreman of the gray-clad squad, bags of powder were placed under the aircraft, and the ship promptly blown up. With large sledge hammers, pieces of the motor and interior fitting still intact were demolished, put into carts, taken away, and dumped over the mole-head into the sea.

The newspapers next day reported that the trial of the Zeppelin X resulted in disaster and total destruction.

In a year the world knew that passenger-carrying Zeppelins were operating successfully in Germany; any one could ride on them—any one who had the price. But no one except trusted men ever intimately saw a military Zeppelin of the type X.

During the time between the destruction of Zeppelin X to the outbreak of the present war, Germany was secretly manufacturing parts of these great machines, but in peace time, except for secret experimental purposes, they were never assembled. All that the world knew about the German Zeppelins were the unwieldly ships that traveled the skies from Düsseldorf along the

Rhine. No military Zeppelin was allowed to exist. This is one of the ways Germany guards her secrets of war.

It is inspection day at the Krupp factories in Essen an der Ruhr. Twice a year the Emperor in person, or his heir apparent, inspects the war arsenals and manufactories in his empire. The most important is the supposed-to-be-private firm, being absolutely, as far as the manufacturing and selling of material and implements of war are concerned, under the control of the government. The present nominal head of the concern is Frau Anna Krupp von Bohlen-Halbach, the only surviving child of the founder of the firm. She receives upwards of $1,000,000 per annum as her share of interest from the works. After the Franco-Prussian War, the firm of Krupp began to be subsidized by the German government, but it was only after the supposed death of the head of the firm that the State assumed absolute control.

The death of Frederick Krupp has never been satisfactorily proven. An undisputable fact is that the coffin resting in the Krupp Mausoleum contains a body bearing as much resemblance to

Frederick Krupp as does the mummy of Ptolemy the Second in the Museum in London. Herr Krupp, who had made the acquaintance in Bad Nauheim of the extremely fascinating Mme. X——, a relative of a high French government official, suddenly contracted a deathly illness. Men of prominence, and in possession of vital state secrets, ere now have found interest in French ladies conducive to sudden ill health.

The royal party, after being received with due honors, commenced its tour of inspection, going with extreme care into the minutest details in those sheds where actual gun making was in progress. Before one of the long factory buildings the party paused and only the Emperor with his chiefs-of-staff, the director of the works, and the master mechanic entered, the rest of the large retinue remaining without. Nothing startling was seen in the interior, only some fifty or sixty large steel blocks, twenty feet long, five feet deep and five feet broad. These blocks were resting in troughs from which the acrid fumes of sulphuric acid arose. Half a dozen elderly, gray-haired workmen were continuously spraying the heavy pieces of steel till they shone like burnished silver.

These huge blocks of metal caused a good deal of quiet speculation amongst the workmen and more than a little anxious inquiry from members of the various foreign secret service. Although some goodly sums were offered at one time or another for definite information, nothing was forthcoming, for no one outside the chosen few really knew. They were too short for crank shafts of battleships or liners; they were too big for axletrees, or even the largest size of field guns thought possible. The Kaiser and his Chief-of-Staff were walking up and down the long lane of these carefully tended, shining masses of steel, the latter repeatedly whispering to his master, bringing a grimly satisfied smile to the Emperor's face.

William II, war lord of Europe, was smiling, and no wonder, for these inoffensive-looking, inert masses of metal were the parent blocks of the mighty 42-centimeter guns, destined to prove such a destructive factor to the most modern fortifications.

This is but another instance of how Germany guards her war secrets. Germany, of all nations, knows that no matter how carefully a secret is kept, it is bound to leak out sooner or later. That is why she did not dare to manufacture or complete a single 42-centimeter gun or war Zeppelin during peace time.

There was unusual activity in the navy yards at Kiel. Prince Henry of Prussia, brother of the Kaiser and Gross Admiral (grand admiral) of the Imperial navy; Admiral von Tirpitz, Minister for Marine, and Rear Admiral von Koster, Chief of the Naval Staff, were on a special tour of inspection. With the usual Prussian thoroughness they went over the whole of the navy yards. Presently the entire party boarded a tender and proceeded to a rocky island, guarding the entrance of the Schley-Bucht (Bay of the Schley), and halted before a small floating drydock anchored inside a narrow, almost inapproachable inlet.

Gray-clad, close-cropped human automatons, similar to those employed at the aero station at Swinemunde, were at work about a squat object, looking like an elongated tadpole, even to the oddappearing appendage, in this instance clearly indicating the rudder. On a little plateau to the right of the landing steps were some stone slabs inscribed with a number and date, the nameless burying ground of the silent workmen. They were life convicts. Germany uses a number of these men for the secret manufacture of certain things. They are well treated, but never regain their personal liberty.

The inspectors entered the fish-like looking craft, which slid easily into the water, diving almost immediately. The submarine, for such it really was, returned after an absence of about three hours. That the experts on reappearing were evidently well satisfied with the prowess of the boat, was clearly indicated by their animated, almost excited comments.

"A cruising range of 4000 miles," the construction officer was jubilantly reporting.

Equipped with a heavy oil engine of 2000 horsepower, an electric motor of 900 horsepower, the new type of submarine was a revelation in naval construction. Up to this time the largest German submarine, U-20, built in 1912, had a motor of only 650 horsepower and a cruising radius of 2000 miles. Naval experts of countries other than Germany had believed that that sized engine was the limit for an undersea boat. But the new type was almost twice as large. It had special construction, with high bows that would enable it to remain on the surface in the heaviest sea. Equipped with three periscopes, it also carried a novelty of naval construction. The unusually high conning tower was fitted with a small lookout cap. This was to revolutionize submarine warfare. At dawn or dusk, when the light is bad, a periscope is as good as useless. With the submarine running awash, however, the lookout, by using the cap atop the conning tower, could clearly see the surrounding sea. This meant that henceforth the German submarine could attack at dawn or twilight unhampered by the difficulties of light that would bother the submarines of all the other navies in the world. Moreover, the new type was able to carry eight torpedoes. Germany had devised disappearing platforms upon which were mounted two fourteen-pounder, quick-firing guns and two one-pounder aeroplane guns. The crew of thirty-five officers and men, the new boat was double the power of any submarine in the world.

The same thing happened now as on the occasion of the trial flight of the super-Zeppelin.

The super-submarine was promptly destroyed. Superior to any submarine in the world, as this war has shown, able to remain two weeks away from its base—not traveling, of course, all the time—equipped with torpedo tubes amidships, as well as at the extremities, it was an innovation in naval construction. What, with its new process for purifying air; its new engine, capable of out-speeding any known submarine eight knots to the hour, this craft upon its successful trial trip instantly ceased to exist. Separately its parts were made and stored. Prussia knows how to guard her military secrets well.

This was the third secret, and perhaps most potent arrow, prepared and kept against "Der Tag!" (The Day—the daily toast in the mess-rooms of His Imperial Majesty's navy).

Captain zur See von Tapken, head of the Intelligence Department of the Imperial navy, was walking restlessly up and down his official quarters at Koeniggratzer strass 70, in Berlin. Frequent glances at a magnificent Orloff clock clearly indicated he was expecting a visitor. Answering the ringing telephone at his desk, the captain sank into his chair with a relieved, "Ah, here he is." An orderly showed Ehrenkrug into the room.

"At last, Herr von Ehrenkrug. We have been waiting for the last two hours," was his greeting.

Ehrenkrug, apologizing, explained that he had

been kept at the Wilhelmstrasse, in Count Wedell's chambers, awaiting the arrival of the Kaiser.

"Ah, you have seen *Seine Majestät* this morning?" von Tapken half queried.

The curt answer, "I had the honor," made the captain smile, and drew the rejoinder,

"I see, Freiherr, you have taken the third degree in our order of the 'Must-Be-Silent' ones. Now let us get to work. You have received your instructions, have you not?" Receiving a nod, he continued: "My instructions were to see that you were thoroughly coached in the topography of the seacoast, so that you may be in a position to direct the charting of our planned depots. I have detailed two of our foremost topographists and oceanographists as your instructors so that you will be familiar with the part of the coast on which we wish to make these depots. Absolute exactitude to the smallest detail is necessary. You will have the service of our local agents there; I have not yet decided which of our diving experts shall accompany you; time enough for that, as it will take you about a month to become familiar with the subject. I do not know the reason why you, a nonprofessional seaman, have been chosen. That rests with those above. What I again impress upon you is minutest care and correct description. I shall now introduce you to your instructors."

Ringing a bell, he commanded an orderly to summon First Lieutenant X———[1] and Navigation Commander Z———. After introducing Ehrenkrug to the above-named officers, von Tapken, in the terse, curt language of a Prussian official, instructed:

"It is commanded that you teach and instruct this gentleman daily from 10 to 12 o'clock and from 3 to 6, on the subjects which were indicated to you before. You will give Herr von Ehrenkrug additional time should he so request. By special cabinet order you are exempt from all other duties. That is all, gentlemen."

The two officers, saluting, withdrew. Offering Ehrenkrug a cigar, and after some pleasant informal chatting about out-of-the-way places, von Tapken proving himself to have been a prodigious traveler and full of unique information, Ehrenkrug took his departure.

Daily, from eight to ten hours, the two officers

[1] Noblesse oblige compels one to withhold names at times.—Author.

and Ehrenkrug pored over huge charts of practically the whole of the British Isles. Sectional maps, giving every foot of ground in certain strategical quarters, were consulted, and minute measurements made, but the most attention was paid to the depth of the different harbor entrances, and especially to the shoals and plateaus lying near the coast. Point after point was selected, until gradually the whole of the British Isles was surrounded by a network of dots, indicating under-sea depots, to be used as supply stations for German submarines.

The great General Staff neglects nothing, quite aware that England's mighty resources would play a deciding factor in a European war. They also thoroughly understood that to eliminate England from the more and more imminent struggle, necessitated two things: either an active invasion of England, or, failing that, the intimidation of Great Britain by air raids and under-sea attacks, not only on her war fleets, but on a much more vulnerable point—her food supply. Germany had realized that it was hopeless to try to build against Great Britain, for whenever Germany built one dreadnought, the British Admiralty laid down two. Germany had made the attempt, but soon realized that even her science and economy could not keep pace with England's wealth and resources, so she cast about for other means. She found them in the invention of Zeppelin, Diesel, and Simon Lake.

Otto Diesel had perfected an internal combustion motor, three times more powerful to its weight than any other known engine in the world. He had submitted his machine to the experts of the German government, who promptly bought the secret. Diesel received one million marks in cash, besides a life rent of twenty thousand thaler. Like a good many others, Diesel, on acquiring this sudden wealth, grew avaricious. It became known to those whose business it is to know these things, that Diesel was on the point of going to England with the intention of further capitalizing his invention. He boarded a steamer at Antwerp, en route to Harwich. He was never seen again. Diesel should have known better, for he had dealt with those "who neither rest nor sleep."

Simon Lake, an American, was the inventor of a number of submarine improvements which his own government did not consider worth while. Over in Germany they had longer heads, and promptly embodied and improved his ideas. It is curious that two of Germany's most powerful trump cards, her submarines and her 42-centimeter guns, originated right here in America, which sets one to wondering at the short-sightedness of the powers that be.

The admiralty division of the great General Staff was at work on a plan whereby German submarines could take supplies at given points from under-sea depots. Although their latest type of submarine has a radius of well over 1,000 miles, and carries six torpedoes, it was still insufficient for an effective blockade of the British coast, for most of the German bases are between 600 and 800 miles away. As it was essential for these sea scorpions to keep an unceasing vigil, it was necessary to find means to replenish fuel, food, and ammunition closer to their sphere of activity. The ordinary way, by means of tenders, was out of the question, for Great Britain "rules the waves," so after perfecting devices for the taking on of stores underneath the water, Germany made plans to plant these stores at convenient points all around Great Britain's shores. At no time in all her history had England faced a greater menace.

The Zeppelin a reality; a gun of forty-two

centimeters, at which the experts of the world had laughed, demonstrated practical; a submarine that could cruise for two weeks away from its base; supply depots planted around the English coast; the inventors safe—Zeppelin unquestionably loyal, Krupp and Diesel disappeared from the earth, alive or dead no man knows; Lake making money and satisfied; Germany had all her military secrets well guarded and ready for The Day.

Those who knew the Kaiser well thought he was growing younger. In all the years he had been in the Emperor's secret service Bertram von Erhenkrug had never seen His Majesty so free from care. One noticed about him a calm confidence that ceased to be held under bounds; it was as if Wilhelm II felt his power, longed to tell, but did not dare tell the world how strong he was. He was ready. By the custom of his house he could go to war, but he did not want war—not yet. He would bide his time, and then he would smash them.

In the early spring of 1914 there came a summons to the agricultural experts of Germany. They met His Majesty in the Royal Palais. They had come prepared to make long reports to him, and as they left, as if to confirm something he said, "Gentlemen, I can rely upon your statement that the crops to be harvested this fall will be the largest in the history of Germany?"

They assured him that this was so.

"That is good."

But through the thin walls of European council chambers the news traveled swiftly. In a room in Downing Street there sat a cold inscrutable Englishman who was glad to know that Germany's crop was a great one, and the Englishman sent one of the King's messengers to France, and another to Belgium, and another to Russia. And Wilhelm II, who had so long been held back by the secret mandate of the Hohenzollerns, thought that he was going to have all of Germany's crop in the barns and that then—for his day was drawing near.

CHAPTER IX

FINE AND EDGED TOOLS

NEARER and nearer drew *Der Tag*. One frantic attempt after another was made by the Kaiser to burst the bonds of his isolation. The situation had changed, and with a vengeance. From 1900 to 1906 it was England who was "splendidly isolated." But thanks to the tactful far-sightedness of Edward VII and his advisers, the situation had undergone an almost miraculous change. The Kaiser's clever coup in bringing the Morocco affair up to a crisis through the Agadir incident, drove the enemy into the open. It showed him that England and France were shoulder to shoulder; he brought about a secret meeting in the Black Forest which Viscount Haldane and Winston Churchill attended *incognito,* and tried to smash the Triple Entente. He found it as firm as a rock.

Now it was Germany's turn to feel *musht* (an Indian hunting term for an outlawed elephant). As all Indian *shikarees* know, these outlawed

163

beasts are the most vicious and dangerous alive, attacking anybody and anything in sight. Much the same, Germany was running amuck. At first the friendly visits of Haldane to the Kaiser's court had tricked the Wilhelmstrasse into believing that a close understanding had been reached with Great Britain. But in the face of existing conditions it would seem as though the charming viscount had been but a screen behind which moved the shrewd, calculating Sir Edward Grey. Germany, to use a poker term, had almost put her cards upon the table during that conference in the Black Forest; almost—but not quite, for with the same Teutonic philosophical craft practised by Herman, the *cherusker,* who lured Varus, the commander of the Roman legions, into a false security and destruction in the *Teutoburger Wald,* so did Germany wisely fool England. Forty-two-centimeter guns, Zeppelins, Diesel motors, and submarines were kept up her sleeve.

It may have been better for the peace of the world in general and for Germany in particular if she had shown to her would-be ally the tremendous resources at her disposal. Perhaps England would have not been quite so eager in taking up the cudgels for the so-called neutrality of Belgium. Plainly the overtures led to no tangible result, and it became evident that Germany was being diplomatically outgeneraled. Realizing the impossibility of weening England over to her side, Germany inaugurated a terrific campaign of espionage in England.

Bertram von Ehrenkrug was closeted with Count von Wedell, the Emperor's chief of the Secret Service, in his chamber in the Wilhelmstrasse, the German Foreign Office. The Count was very insistent and emphatic in his instructions. Plainly these instructions were not much to Ehrenkrug's liking. The Count, well versed in reading the facial expressions of his fellow men, was not slow in discerning his unwilling attitude; for he sternly remarked, "It is no use kicking, Ehrenkrug; this has to be done and the Emperor has decided on you to do it. Besides, you have already received a pretty good schooling in what is now required of you. Haven't you learned yet to separate private and ethical scruples from the work and missions which you are bidden to undertake? Is it necessary to point out to you of all men the dire necessity which compels us to do these things?"

Ehrenkrug chose not to reply, and Wedell continued, "Daily the activities of our enemy become more apparent. No one knows how soon we may have to face terrific odds which will need our utmost strength and resources to combat. We may have to face these odds alone; that is why we need every and all information we can get. That is why we spare no effort or money in preparing ourselves. There is no need for sophistry. The Emperor knows, I know, you know, that the necessity for these things is unethical . . ." The Count shrugged. "But as long as this necessity remains we have to do it—and will. Besides, we only use the same weapons which are used against us; perhaps"—this with a grim smile—"our weapons are the finer tempered."

Knowing the futility of argument or of opposition, Ehrenkrug nodded a silent consent.

The Count pressed a button and ordered the attendance of the oceanographic expert in charge of the English coast sections. The officer in question appearing, the three went over once more the field of Ehrenkrug's prospective activity. The Count pointed out various strategical spots on and off the coast of Great Britain which the German admiralty deemed necessary for submarine attacks on England. These strategic points, about five hundred miles apart, as previously indicated, were intended for submarine depots. The latest type of German submarines, as yet not even constructed, included devices which enabled them to take fuel and ammunition while submerged. The Count also instructed Ehrenkrug to sound his English acquaintances in every way, shape or form on their sympathies, tendencies to support the Government; in fact, on any phase likely to have bearing on the political or diplomatic situation in England.

One of the greatest assets which Germany has assiduously promulgated, especially the great General Staff, is the acquisition of an enormous mass of information gained by observant German travelers in all parts of the world. Every German officer on furlough as well as most German commercial travelers are trained and requested by their respective departments to send essays, abstracts, and reports of their observations to headquarters. This information is sifted, compared, and the result carefully docketed and pigeon-holed for future reference. The mass of information thus gained apart from that gathered by the Secret Service direct, is past all believing. It is to a great extent responsible for

Germany's success in keeping the world at bay, and her ability to inflict losses upon her enemies in the least expected quarters.

On his way over to England, Ehrenkrug had plenty of time for cogitations. They were decidedly unpleasant, for a man engaged in such dangerous and unpleasant tasks is apt to hold executive sessions with himself conducive to anything but a placid frame of mind. Gradually, in the course of his mission, Ehrenkrug had been drawn deeper and deeper into the shadier sides of the Secret Service. Not that this service is at any time very aseptic. It needs a good deal of antiseptics in the form of patriotism, necessity, force, or greed to make it at all tolerable. By birth, breeding, and personal inclination, Ehrenkrug was anything but a born schemer. However, once in the meshes of this service there is no drawing back. The instances where one has been able to withdraw with a whole skin are few and far between. As regards one's reputation, that invariably comes out in tatters. Ehrenkrug knew all this, but having in the course of his wanderings become more or less of a fatalist, he shrugged his shoulders and went ahead.

It was the height of the hunting season in England. At W——, the hunting lodge of the Earl of R——, one of the leading sportsmen in the United Kingdom, visitors were arriving daily. The small somnolent station and village of W——, named after his lordship's estate, were in the throes of their annual excitement.

These time-honored hunting parties in England are the means of bringing together the various members of the British aristocracy. At no other time, unless it be on the race meetings, does the ultra-stiff and conservative Englishman of birth and breeding unbend to such an extent as on these meets. He becomes almost Bohemian on such occasions and meets in good fellowship even "bally" foreigners, you know, especially if those "bally Johnnies" know how to ride or shoot. Neither intellectual attainments in sciences, arts, and literature nor the possession of wealth or family origin impresses an Englishman as does excellence in one of the classical sports such as riding to hounds, shooting, or cricket. Ehrenkrug, thanks to his natural fondness for all sorts of sports and his training in one of the crack cavalry regiments of Germany, soon found himself the admired center of Lord R——'s hunting party.

Tall, good looking, of a distinctive clean-cut type, invitations to other shooting and house parties were freely extended to this distinguished foreigner. Here Ehrenkrug was able to lay the foundation of a circle of acquaintances of immeasurable benefit to him in obtaining all sorts of information useful to the German government.

Quietly and unobtrusively he made the acquaintance of men and women in a position to supply the wanted information. Gradually, through close study, he was able to weed out the most likely persons to be approached. He would observe their personal habits, note the extravagant losses of some of the men and women at bridge and baccarat, make inquiries as to their financial standing, and then instruct subagents to buy up, if possible, their various notes of hand (I O U's), and mortgages. Ehrenkrug never played himself, but would introduce others very willing to gamble with and accommodate with great alacrity the persons selected for approach. Gradually the fine invisible net was drawn tighter and tighter around these jelly-boned drones of humanity. Then one fine morning a gentleman with a distinctly Hebraic physiognomy would introduce himself. This gentleman would produce a sheaf of I O U's and mortgages, and ruthlessly press for settlement, which in five cases out of ten these dupes were unable to meet. This favorable time was then astutely used in hinting various ways by which the obligation might be wiped out and canceled. The victims, carefully chosen and at their wits' ends, in seven cases out of ten would sell their honor and country for the means of being able to maintain their station in society, said society being the only god they worship. It is by such means that the innermost secrets and information of even royal households are obtained. And it was by employing just such means that Ehrenkrug was able to obtain the plans of the *Ajax* and *Queen Mary,* the two latest dreadnoughts of the British navy.

Of course the introduction of the German agents into British society is always engineered directly by the Secret Service officials in Berlin, although never without the knowledge of the local German embassy. There was the case of the spurious Countess von B——, whose mysterious career in London ended before His Worship de Rutzen, the famous London police magistrate. The then German ambassador to the Court of St. James naturally disclaimed all knowledge of the woman in question, but on more than one occasion both attended the same social function, were introduced formally, and seemed to be able to make passable party conversation!

Sometimes the Kaiser in person, through reasons of his own, introduced members of his staff and suite by *quasi*-forcing them on to the society folk. This was evident in the instance of the Emperor's last visit to England prior to the death of Queen Victoria. The visit was not the outcome of an invitation given to him, but in consequence of a wish expressed by him that he might be invited. The Prince of Wales sent an unofficial, private message through a friend in Berlin to the following effect: "Tell him that my mother's precarious state of health will unable her to entertain him, but I will do all in my power to make him welcome and his stay a pleasant one. There is one favor I would ask, however, and this is that he shall not bring Admiral von Seden Bibrian." [1]

When the Emperor arrived with his retinue of sixty, Admiral von Seden Bibrian was conspicuous among them. The large number of the Em-

[1] Admiral von Seden Bibrian had spoken most disrespectfully about the Prince, criticizing in a coarse manner the Prince's attention to a certain court lady.

peror's suite on this, as well as on other occasions, the Emperor having visited England fourteen times, outran the accommodations of Windsor Castle, and a number of his officers and secretaries were of necessity lodged and quartered upon the estates round about. A clever ruse this, for it brought these men trained to observe any and everything in close contact with various possible means of information. This practise gave rise afterwards to some ill-natured gossip and cartoons which, coming to the ears of King Edward, caused him to exclaim, "We can get along with the Russians, the Japanese, even the Americans, in short with everybody, but these people are simply impossible."

Ehrenkrug's exploits on this one mission, if told in detail, would fill several chapters. One incident will suffice, however, to show the crafty methods employed by German secret agents in using English society folk as unwitting collaborators. Ehrenkrug arranged a cruising party around the northern coast of the British Isles. He selected a congenial group of companions— men and women well known in English society, amongst them several officers and their wives. The boat was commodious, and it had a well-stocked provision locker—in fact, everything necessary for a highly enjoyable cruise. Having seen to it that they brought their cameras along, Ehrenkrug, after the first day out, soon had the party converted into enthusiastic camera fiends. In and out the bays and inlets to John O'Groat's the steamer leisurely cruised, and at each point numberless photographs were taken so that practically a continuous panorama could have been made of them if pieced together; yet each was so taken as to bring in the salient landmarks and coastal contours. Naturally Ehrenkrug was not so poor a host as to keep his guests waiting for the finished results of their photographic expeditions; he had provided a dark room below in charge of an expert. The expert, needless to say, was one of Ehrenkrug's subagents, and the first prints of every photograph taken are to-day docketed in the *Admiralstab's* archives in Berlin.

The same sort of tactics that were employed by the Kaiser on his English visits were used in the memorable journey of the Crown Prince to India, although there were other reasons for his leaving Germany at the time.

The Crown Prince's indiscretion in going to the Reichstag and loudly applauding the violently anti-English speeches of some of the members, although received with great public acclamation, displeased the Government and most of all his royal father. It was deemed advisable to remove the Crown Prince's disturbing influence for the time being and the grand tour of the heir of the throne of Germany to India was decided upon. With true Hohenzollern craft they decided to kill two birds with one stone. This tour would broaden His Imperial Highness's mind and give him experience; it also could be made an investigation of the political sentiments of the Prince of India.

The British government was somewhat in a quandary. The visit of the Crown Prince of Germany to British possessions of the East was submitted to them as an entirely unofficial health and hunting trip of His Imperial Highness. Not even a German warship was going to be used, but a Nord German-Lloyd steamer—very clever this! But England had some previous experiences of unofficial German visitors and was by no means enthusiastic over the proposal. A lack of cordiality and warmth, however, does not disconcert any German project. What could the British government do? Grin and bear it. His Majesty's Government is pleased to extend to His Imperial Highness, the Crown Prince Frederick William, the hospitality of the Indian Empire, and will do all in its power to make His Imperial Highness's hunting trip a successful one. Thus officially; unofficially the Secret Service of India was strengthened by some of the cleverest and shrewdest service officers in the employ of the Secretary for India. England may be a fool as far as European Secret Service is concerned, but in Indian affairs she takes no chances; that's a horse of a different color. "We'll jolly well see that His Nibs doesn't *miss* his Shikari," was the comment, somewhat cryptic to an outsider, but to an insider deuced lucid—of one of the Anglo-Indian officials to the author.

The first place where the Crown Prince made any lengthy stay was at the Island of Ceylon. Thanks to the munificent hospitality of that merchant prince, Herr Froudenberg, Consul General for Germany in Ceylon, and the combined efforts of other wealthy German and colonial houses, the Prince's stay in this pearl of the British crown was like a continuous dream out of "The Thousand and One Nights." Very interesting stories could be related of what befell certain very pretty little American tourists during this visit, but as they have no political significance, they need not be elaborated on here.

The Prince landed at Bombay and became the guest of the Indian government. Forthwith an exhaustive and elaborate hunting program was gone through, but it was noticed that the Prince was not permitted to meet any of the native princes and rajahs except at some semi-state functions. Adroitly the officials frustrated the repeated attempts of the German party to be received at private entertainments by prominent Indians. In one case only was the vigilance of the service officers frustrated when the Gaegwar of Baroda met the Prince in private. There is not the slightest doubt that Anglo-Indian government officials heaved a big sigh of relief when the smoke of His Imperial Highness's departing steamer gradually merged with the horizon.

Directly this visit would seem to have had no political significance; indirectly it did. The Prince's suite was not without its coterie of Indian experts who were able to feel out the sympathies of the natives in the event of hostilities between Germany and Britain. Moreover, had not his royal papa gone reverently sandaled into the Grand Moshee at Constantinople and had he not been given the green scarf of an Hadji, which is granted only to the true believers who make the pilgrimage to Mecca? It is significant to note that not many moons passed between the departure of the Kaiser's son and the arrival of King George in India for the Durbar. It was not good for England's prestige in India to permit the native to be impressed for too long or too deeply with the majestic appearance of the future ruler of Germany.

Germany had worked her way with these fine and edged tools of the Secret Service in every corner of the globe. How necessary it has been for her to use them is brought home forcibly to the American public through the continually cropping up of episodes such as the attempt to blow up the international Canadian bridge, the Stegler case and the Swaboda incident. Previous to the outbreak of the war there was scarcely any necessity for the activity of Secret Service agents and spies in this country—Brussels, Copenhagen, Monte Carlo, and of course all the capitals of Europe being the hotbeds of espionage activity. Since the outbreak of the European war all of these avenues have been closed and the central point of gravity, by reason of the commercial activity of the United States, has been shifted over here. The uninterrupted commercial relations of the United States give great facilities to the agents of foreign governments to obtain information and transmit the same through the various business houses, often unknown to the heads of these concerns. It is a fact that the powers in Europe and especially Germany obtain information about things happening within a hundred miles of their own firing line through these mediums and via New York. This country at present swarms with men and women in the pay of one government or another. It is true that in most instances they do not violate the neutrality or interests of the United States, that is, as yet; in which instance they would not hesitate a moment to injure the United States. It is all very well to be lenient and to point to the freedom clauses in the Constitution, but the author would like to sound here a note of warning. He knows from his own experience the ruthless disregard of consequences demanded of and practised by these emissaries. It may prove advisable for the Government to look into and curtail their activities.

CHAPTER X

JUMBLED INTERESTS

ALTHOUGH the political barometer stood at its lowest level, there were still men in Europe who did not believe an outbreak of hostilities possible. The long reign of peace in Europe had lulled certain nations into a false security. Commercialism and finance during forty years of undisputed sway had flattered itself that it possessed power strong enough to prevent a general upheaval. Idealistic dreamers, philanthropists and peace advocates, who had spent millions on peace propagandas and temples for the White Dove, had added their quota in obscuring the real trend of affairs to such an extent that those who correctly read the signs of the times and warned against them were put down as alarmists and militarists. In no country was this more apparent than in England.

Men like Lord Roberts of Kandahar, Baden-Powell, Admiral Fisher, Lord Kitchener of Khartoum and many other able men in other spheres and walks of life had raised their voices time and time again against the almost suicidal dawdling of the peace-pifflers. The smug self-sufficiency of the English "pepper bags" with characteristic short-sightedness and stupidity pooh-poohed these warnings as the ravings of military glory-mad alarmists. Deeming themselves secure in the possession of their money bags and with a wisdom arising therefrom, they tied their purse strings and effectively defeated the efforts of men more far-sighted than themselves.

It is a lucky thing for England that the efforts of the above mentioned men, although receiving very little or no official assistance, were able to arouse a certain amount of public sentiment resulting in the formation of independent training camps, rifle clubs, etc., which organizations have been able at short notice to place 200,000 fighting men at the disposal of the Government. They have proved second to none in the firing line, much to the astonishment and discomfiture of the German General Staff who could or would not believe the efficiency of the British non-official soldier. But more of this in another chapter.

In Germany an entirely different condition of affairs existed. Proposals of peace, disarmament and arbitration were patiently listened to and promptly disregarded. This, not because of any Teutonic love for strife and bloodshed in the abstract, but from a deep-rooted conviction that now, as in ages past, international affairs would have to be decided by the sword. Germany of all nations, while recognizing the blessings of peace and tranquillity, realized that the devoutly to be hoped for millennium is as far off to-day, if not farther, than it was in the days of the Punic Wars. A lot of twaddle has been discharged upon long suffering humanity about Germanic aggression, militarism, etc., said literature being assiduously distributed by her equally guilty enemies.

These theories and effusions as to the cause and prevention of wars, with their high-toned rhetorical involvedness, seem to lose sight of the main factor of all things existent, in nationalities and creeds, in individuals and masses: human nature. If two thousand years of the most logical and beneficial teachings of a creed purposedly and admittedly trying to instil meekness, forbearance and brotherhood has been unable to eliminate strife, dissension and bloodshed from their own ranks, is it to be wondered at that a nation, naturally given to deep thoughts and studies, rejects as impracticable the propositions made by more or less interested theorists?

The powers that be in Germany hold with the axiom that he who strikes first wins half the battle. So convinced were they of the ultimate necessity for settling the decision of the great European question through a force of arms that they were quite prepared to act the part of the aggressor if necessary.

The whole situation, calmly and logically reviewed, points plainly to this undisputable fact: Germany, under the rule of her three Hohenzollern emperors, has attained a foremost position among the nations through having been undisturbed by any wars for over forty years. During these forty years she has, through application, thoroughness and science, built up a commercial position second to none, and that in opposition to nations which had entered the field hundreds of years previously.

Habitually and fundamentally there is no race on earth more fond of the ease of life and all things pertaining thereto than the Teuton. No race, unless it be the Chinese, is more unwilling to violently physically exert themselves than the

Germanic. Physical prowess, almost idolized in other countries, is relegated very much to the background. In the automatically slow progress of commerce and science Germany had no reason to fear another nation on earth. She could and in fact did hold more than her own; but with metaphysical insight derived from and fostered through a close study of human history and philosophy, she recognized a possibly violent interruption of peaceful advancement. With Teutonic resignation to that which they considered inevitable the German people set about to prepare for and guard against "The Day." They went about this with characteristically ruthless thoroughness.

The marvelous efficiency and resisting power of the German army [1] is the outcome of a mathematical system working with clock-like regularity and precision. This system permeates collectively the whole empire, but individually rests on the thorough training of each unit and individual. From his early childhood in the parental home, the German child is taught the fundamental lessons of obedience. From the Emperor's palace

[1] The actual fighting strength of Germany has been described in *The Secrets of the German War Office,* vide chapter "The German War Machine," page 155.

down to the humblest household, the authority of
the parent is never questioned. The whole life
and system is built around this early training.
From the moment a child leaves his home to attend school, where also a rigid, unquestioning
obedience to his teachers is demanded, through
the early period of manhood as an apprentice in
the various branches of the trades and profes-
sions, this discipline goes on. It reaches its highest point when the young man enters the army
or navy.

To an outsider, unacquainted with Teutonic
ideals, this continuous subservience appears harsh
in the extreme. Without question, it would be
and is irksome to those who are not gradually
brought up and educated under such a régime.
In reality—and this is well understood by German leaders of thought and education—this
mergence of the individual will into a collective
whole is nothing more than a logical outcome of
democratic ideals. That last statement may seem
paradoxical; for how, one might ask, can a monarchy be democratic? The situation is really not
quite so contradictory as it would at first appear.
The basic principle of democracy: "one for all
and all for one," is insisted and acted upon every-

where in monarchical Germany. The State stands *in loco parentis*. This is visible in the entire range of public life. For decades Germany has embodied and used ideas such as State ownership of railways, post and telegraph, highways, waterways, canal, etc., ideas that so far have only been advocated, much less adopted, in presumably democratic or republican countries. Thus, in Germany, State ownership is operated for the benefit of the nation and not for the exploitation of the same. To this truly democratic system, in the main, is due Germany's success as a commercial nation, and that in the face of a distinctly unfavorable geographical position and a great handicap in natural resources.

It is a strange fact that in this monarchical Germany all advanced ideals and cults have found fruitful generation. Consider Socialism, Syndicalism, Communism, Local Self-Government. You will find them all flourishing independently, and yet collectively working together for the benefit of the whole and of what the nation conceives to be for the best. That is why there is found in Germany the best and most up-to-date government. That is why even under the tremendous strain of huge armaments, taxation is lower in

Germany than in most other countries. That is why Socialism in face of all suppositions and predictions stands solidly behind the Government in this present struggle.

The Teuton is an idealist and somewhat of a mystic dreamer, but his idealism is intensely practical. He keeps his feet firmly planted on earth although his head may be in the clouds. You have only to read (and digest—if you can!) Schiller, Goethe, Schopenhauer, Schlegel and Kant, or to listen to Wagner's music and plays to realize the complexity of the Teutonic character. Their art, philosophy and music, even their wildest imagery, is built around a very tangible materialism.

This utilitarianism finds its embodiment in the House of Hohenzollern. Go back into history and come down to the present day; strip the Hohenzollerns, especially the reigning head thereof, of all superficial pomp, circumstance and pose, and you will find a solid core of downright business ability, absolutely necessary in the government of such an intensely practical race as the Teutonic. By the same token the very intenseness of their materialism demands, true to human nature, a reaction. This reaction is supplied very adequately by William II in his theatrical, often melodramatic, utterances and poses.

All through history the Hohenzollerns, with very few exceptions, have proven themselves to be keen students of the *Zeitgeist* (spirit of the time). Their policies have found it necessary at times to suppress a too virulent or sudden expansion of this "spirit"; but sooner or later they have managed to use and control it for the benefit of themselves and their country. No one has done this more so than the present ruler. The Emperor is by no means the genius which he would make the world believe. His scientific and artistic abilities are open to much criticism, but true to the spirit of the time and with characteristic Hohenzollern shrewdness, he is to-day one of the wealthiest men in the world. Besides being the largest farmer and cattle breeder in Germany, he holds and has held stocks and bonds in the best paying concerns at home and abroad. He has married his sons to the wealthiest princesses in Europe. The Crown Princess Cecile's dowry amounts to no less than $35,000,000 in cash; Prince Eitel Frederick's bride brought him a *Mitgift* of nearly $40,000,000.

First and last, the collective wealth of the

Hohenzollern family is nearly $1,000,000,000. The official income of Emperor William II is $4,500,000; the revenue from Crown Lands, forests and domains is $2,500,000; three investments of the Emperor's before the outbreak of the war brought a net profit of $2,000,000; accumulated interest and moneys from other sources easily total a further couple of millions. It is no exaggeration to compute the Emperor's yearly income at $12,000,000.

Apart from lavish expenditures in the upkeep of his castles, the Emperor is very careful and discriminate in the handling of his cash. The Crown Prince, on the other hand, is quite the opposite. His pronounced ability to incinerate 1000 mark *Scheine* (bills) has often led to some stormy interviews with the imperial papa.

Frederick Wilhelm, whose main claim to notability previous to the outbreak of the war lay in his horsemanship, his judgment of horseflesh and his marked ability to detect the fine anatomical points of the weaker sex, once made a famous bet on the outcome of the Guinea Stakes in England. The bet was for 500,000 marks ($125,000) and the wager was contracted with two prominent members of the British aristocracy.

The Secrets of the Hohenzollerns

The Prince lost. There being some delay in settling the score, the holder of the note, the eldest son of Lord P——, who found himself one day in urgent need of funds, pledged the note of the Crown Prince to a well-known London money lender. The resourceful money lender, after finding of no avail his gently conveyed hints as to liquidation—which probably never reached the Prince—hit upon the following expedient. Amongst his numerous clients he had a lady well connected in both the English and German courts. This lady, somewhat under obligation to him, was requested to be the bearer of a letter to His Imperial Majesty, Emperor Wilhelm. The purpose of the letter as explained to Lady Ch—— was a desire expressed by the sender for His Majesty's gracious acceptance of a very rare old coin, the Emperor having a fad for coin collecting. Certainly, she would be only too glad to, etc., etc. Shortly after, Lady Ch—— left for Berlin. In the course of her stay she received an invitation to a garden party at Sans Souci and thought this the very opportunity to present the missive. Imagine the poor woman's astonishment when, instead of being pleasantly surprised at the supposed offer of a priceless coin, the Emperor, on opening the letter, grew turkey red, and, in his usual brusk manner inquired, "Dash it all, my Lady, since when has the British nobility undertaken to transmit dunning letters? What's the meaning of this, anyhow?"

Fortunately, the Emperor can always see and appreciate a joke, and on hearing Lady Ch——'s explanation he laughed heartily, remarking, "Damn clever of the old fox, eh what? As for that son of mine, I'll take it out of his pocket money."

There is reason to believe that he did, for the Crown Prince was known to be notably short of cash for some time to come. Also His Imperial Highness was intensely displeased with anything English just then, and even kicked his English bulldog out of his quarters.

Some of the biggest financial deals of the last decade were engineered by the royal stockbrokers of Europe and the leading spirit in this most profitable form of employment was none other than Emperor William II. The most notable deal swung by His Imperial Majesty was the floating of the 800,000,000 mark loan for the Krupp Gun Works in Essen. All the Emperor's private friends and cronies were "let in on the ground floor," as for example, the King of Italy with $25,000,000; the Grand Duke of Mecklenburg-Schwerin for $10,000,000. Some of the intimates of the Kaiser in England were also thoughtfully considered. There are to-day quite a number of houses in England, including some very high dignitaries of the Church of England, who derive or did derive up to the outbreak of the war quite an opulent income from this source. One who did not profit by this transaction was Leopold, King of the Belgians. He was not even let in on the top floor! And thereby hangs a tale.

Quite the second keenest royal commission agent in Europe was His Majesty of Belgium. No one amongst his royal brethren knew the value of money better or could spend it faster and enjoy it more. He manipulated quite a few deals of his own, outstanding amongst which was the Congo Rubber Company. Thoughtlessly, in this instance, he neglected to invite to the feast his royal cousin of Germany, who promptly proceeded to spoil the banquet. When large blocks of stock were put for sale on the German markets the bankers, receiving a tip from the Government, showed a distinct inclination to leave the stock severely alone. The general public was antagonized through the publicity judiciously given and distributed via German channels to the more or less true atrocity revelations of Dr. Karl Peters, one time bosom crony of Leopold and dictator-in-chief of the Congo. Having previously milked the Congo dry, the now saintly Peters, receiving but scant treatment from his quondam bosom friend, suddenly blossomed forth as apostle and humanitarian. The result was that the Congo Rubber Company ended in fiasco. Herein lies one of the reasons for the ill-feeling and antagonism between the Hohenzollerns and Coburgs.

Another *casus belli* between those two royal houses and for which Belgium now suffers was the ambition of King Albert to restore the pristine glory and predominance of the Flanders in the Low Countries. The Hohenzollerns, especially William II, put every conceivable obstacle in the way of the ruler of Belgium, as for instance, the marriage of the Queen of Holland to a German prince, frustrating a hope of the Braganzas of making those two countries one.[1]

[1] The author was instrumental in gathering information for the German government anent this most interesting and desired amalgamation.

The Secrets of the Hohenzollerns

The consequent marriage of King Albert of the Belgians to a Bavarian princess was a further disappointment, as it did not bring with it the hoped for German support of his ambitions.

Such a combination of Belgium and Holland would have spelled a further delay in Germany's design to extend her influence further west along the North Sea coast. In the other direction she had a stumbling block in Denmark.

The relations of the Scandinavian countries, Norway, Sweden and Denmark, to Germany are variegated and involved. Denmark, for instance, is distinctly pro-British, somewhat inexplicably so in view of Lord Nelson's feat of the bombardment of Copenhagen. This characteristic piece of English gun-policy was equaled, however, if not outdone by the Prussian maneuvers in 1864 when Denmark lost Schleswig-Holstein. The Danes, like the French, have never been able to forget or reconcile themselves to the loss of these provinces. This Danish antagonism to all things Germanic has been of tremendous benefit to the English campaign in this war; for if Denmark was pliant to German desires, the British fleet would have almost an unmanageable task of keeping the German fleet from breaking through the cordon and smashing the units of the British fleet in detail. As it stands, Germany's only means of shuttle-cocking and concentrating her fleet at any given point is through the Kaiser Wilhelm Canal, the North Sea outlet of which is at Holtenau. This canal enables the German Highsea Fleet to steam from the Baltic into the North Sea and vice versa; this, of course, is well known to the British Admiralty and the North Sea outlet is constantly watched by the most powerful British squadrons. The only other possible outlet from the Baltic is through the Grosse and the Kleine Belt, two narrows leading into the Kattegat and Skagerak and controlled by Denmark. It stands to reason that if Denmark was willing to assist Germany by opening these straits to the German fleets, the forces now watching a single outlet would have to be divided to watch both; in which event these divided fleets would be weaker than the concentrated German Highsea Fleet. The possible results would be disastrous to the English cause. It is another inexplicable blunder on the part of German diplomats that they have not been able to placate Denmark. Here the overweening ego of the Hohenzollerns had frustrated time and again the efforts of far-seeing

German statesmen; whereas the alliance of the Danish royal house with that of England through Queen Alexandra has borne for England some very material results.

In the case of Norway and Sweden the situation is somewhat different. Both these countries, although possessing no phenomenal love for Germany, have a distinct fear of the Northern Colossus that quite outweighs any other consideration. Moreover, Norway and Sweden are vitally interested in crude commercial enterprises due to their natural wealth in minerals, lumber and coal of which three commodities Germany was and is their best customer. It is of paramount interest to them that the Baltic and the northern portion of the North Sea should remain an unrestricted highway, as both countries, considering their size and population, hold the largest shipping interests still. Germany has always fostered and in no ways handicapped Swedish or Norwegian shipping enterprise or industries. A keen observer and traveler of the Baltic seaports of Germany such as Danzig, Stettin, Swinemunde, Rostock and Kiel, as well as Hamburg, must have been struck with the large number of Swedish and Norwegian flags seen in the above mentioned harbors. Besides, since the days of Gustavus Adolphus, the social relations as regards philosophical and religious ideals have run close between these countries. Last and not least is the tremendous influence which the German Emperor personally exerts over Norway and Sweden through his immense popularity and the ownership, nominally vested in the Krupp Company, but in reality controlled by His Majesty in person, of the valuable iron mines. It is a well known fact that outside certain mines in Spain, the iron ore deposits of the Scandinavian Peninsula are the richest and purest in manganese, essential in the manufacture of the highest class of steel goods, especially guns. It is only the fear of the unconquered and as yet little damaged fighting strength of the British navy which keeps those two countries from actively participating and assisting Teutonic ambitions in Central Europe. Meantime, the German Emperor as mine owner is biding his time.

The attitude of Italy in this European holocaust has been a puzzling one to those unacquainted with Italian statecraft and the many-sided undercurrent influences at work, especially the methods of the royal stockbrokers. The idea that Italy should have been true to her obligations under the Triple Alliance became a dead letter with Bismarck's and Signor Crispi's dropping out of office. This was practically the accepted opinion in all European cabinets. The active assistance of Italy was never counted upon by the German General Staff, that is, not at the beginning of any hostilities. Under given circumstance, being paid and getting her price, it was known then as it is known now that Italy would put her deciding weight in the scales on the side of Germany. The question is: what's the price? First and foremost Trieste and the Trentino, also Dalmatia, at present held by Austria; secondly, a solid foothold on North Africa through means of colonial territory, since Italy more than any other European country is in need of adequate colonial possessions; thirdly, the predominate position in the Mediterranean, at present divided between England and France with the scale balanced in favor of England.

Italian statesmen have proven themselves much too shrewd to let such an opportunity for the advancement and benefit of their country as the present to go by. Delve into history and you will find that Italian diplomacy has always managed to be on the winning side and gain quite a good deal in one way or another without actually fighting themselves. By playing the game of "watchful waiting" Italy will gain more in the end than if she were at present to cast in her lot with either side. Without the slightest doubt she will obtain Trieste and the Trentino, for Austria is not in a position to hold out much longer. As previously shown, Italy has made repeated bids for colonial empire in northern Africa, only to be blocked by England and France. Apparently neither France nor England is willing as yet to concede to Italy portions of territory under their control, but Italy must have some such portion, and, by the end of the war, will be found a possession. Thirdly, Italy expects, and reasonably so, to be the predominant factor in the Mediterranean, which, in the event of the defeat of the Allies, she certainly will be. Just now, she is in the third place; with the success of the Allies and the advent of Russia into the possession of the Dardanelles, she would be relegated to the fourth place. Neither a successful England nor France would be willing, unless compelled by dire necessity, to give up their leading position in the Mediterranean. Nor could or would they be able to prevent their ally Russia from asserting a newly acquired predominancy. This is well known to Italy's leading men of affairs, but the clamor of the ignorant masses is likely to rush Italy into this war.

All of this suits the book of Germany extremely well. Recognizing the improbability, nay, almost impossibility of the House of Savoy fighting shoulder to shoulder with the House of Hapsburg under existent circumstances, the very neutrality of Italy is of a measurable benefit to Germany, for Italy can and does supply some of the most needed raw materials, such as sulphur, copper, etc.

Apart from diplomatic and economic reasons, the neutrality of Italy as far as Germany is concerned is still further insured through the close understanding between the House of Savoy and the House of Hohenzollern (for the House of Savoy cannot forget what a good friend Wilhelm proved when he permitted it a place in the Krupp loan),[1] the personal influence of the Kaiser at the Vatican, and the general close social relationship between the two countries. In its way,

[1] The author himself carried the documents relative to this investment to Rome.

the House of Savoy is quite as ambitious as the House of Hohenzollern and, as those two ambitions usually do not clash or interfere with each other, this constitutes another strong current in this maelstrom of jumbled interests.

Strange and conflicting are the conditions existing between the House of Brunswick and that of Hohenzollern. It is a curious fact that, literally speaking, there is more so-called English blood in the present Hohenzollerns than German, and more German blood in the reigning English family than blood of their own. The husband of Queen Victoria, Prince Albert, was a German; the mother of the present Kaiser was an English woman; the mother of the present King of England was a Danish princess of half-German extraction; the mother of the present Prince of Wales, Queen Mary of England, was a Princess of Teck, an old expatriated German family. Perhaps it is just this close relationship which has given rise to the innumerable squabbles and is probably one of the causes for the apparently bitter feeling between these royal houses.

Admittedly, there are no quarrels so bitter as those of the clans; and just as in clan fights, royalty is quite willing to fight—or rather let others fight for them—until their own *mutual* interests are in danger. Then one can observe the strange phenomenon of these apparently individually bitter enemies changing front and making common cause against those who threaten their cherished prerogatives and privileges. The Hohenzollerns, the Hanoverians and the Brunswickers were always more or less good friends. They had too much in common to be at loggerheads. The personal squabbles and petty ambitions amongst themselves were never permitted to obscure or endanger the broader policies of their respective countries. It must have been indeed extraordinarily powerful influences which compelled these royal houses to become openly avowed enemies. But are they openly avowed enemies? Do any of the crowned heads at war to-day bear a personal hatred of their foe?

To the general mass of people the answer would seem: Yes. To those versed in the undercurrents of diplomacy and to a few keen and intelligent watchers of the world's principal actors, the answer is: No. And No, written big. The upstage acting of the royal George in kicking out the divine William's banner from the chapel of the Garter Kings at Arms; the fine byplay of the Kaiser's in tearing off the glittering baubles presented to him on many a convivial feast—for which, by the by, the taxpayers of England had to foot the bill—has and is completely fooling not only their own subjects but the world at large.

Innumerable books, essays, pamphlets and treatises, official and otherwise, have been discharged upon a brain-weary public, setting forth, with more or less clearness and reason, the cause, justification or fault of the present wholesale murder. The greater number of these effusions have for their main object the strengthening of an individual claim; and, all or most of them succeed in bewildering still more an already sorely befuddled public. That is just what they are intended to do: to keep the real cause of this satanic carnage hidden from those who are laying down their *Blut and Gut*. Otherwise they may think twice about doing it. Even a half thought on the part of those who should think, but will not, would stop all wars more effectively than the building of a thousand peace palaces. This applies to Germany as well as to France and England. It is not good to let the common people think too much. This is one of the basic rules of the Hohenzollerns. This is the foundation principle of every throne in Europe. In the jumble of European political and royal financial deals, the interests of the common soul are utterly lost.

CHAPTER XI

THE BREWING STORM

THE month of July was unusually hot and sultry. All Nature was drooping under the stifling atmosphere. Those wise in the ways of Nature presaged a terrific thunderstorm, albeit there was never a cloud in the sky. And the general political conditions in Europe were almost an exact counterpart of the atmospheric conditions. The situation between the leading powers on the Continent had gradually arrived at such a pass that none of them exactly knew where they were or what would happen next.

Economic conditions in Germany without being bad were by no means good. The phenomenal commercial prosperity starting about 1895 and increasing by leaps and bounds up to its zenith in 1912 was toning down somewhat. The unprecedented influence of wealth had created an unheard-of taste for luxury and the prodigal spending of money, practises as a rule foreign to the frugal Teutonic temperament. Workshops and factories which had sprung up like mushrooms in a warm April shower and which had been working for ten years at full blast, employing a vast number of men and paying a scale of wages previously unknown in the history of German manufacturing, found it necessary to curtail their activities to a considerable extent. Most of these industrial institutions had been running along on borrowed capital, lent, in many instances, by the State, and were suffering through overproduction consequent on the existent general trade depressions. The Government, hard taxed by the ever-increasing army and navy expenditures, was unable to carry both burdens with any degree of safety, and began curtailing, not on army and navy budgets, but on the wholesale assistance of commercial enterprises. The resultant reaction created a serious and distracting restlessness and discontent amongst all classes. As yet no actual pinch was felt, for with true Teutonic thrift, the great mass of the people had used the fifteen fat years to store up a vast amount of savings.

The political situation was likewise involved and by no means satisfactory. That Germany was being forced into an almost complete isolation was well known to those at the head of affairs. The Emperor was aware of the existence of a strong alliance between England, France and Russia. This alliance, without being pleasing, was at least recognized and provided against. But the concerted efforts of England and France to draw Italy and Japan into the coalition against her acted on Germany much in the same manner that a *banderillera* frenzies an already half-mad bull. The war party comprising the gun and powder interests (Germany, by the way, manufactures and controls more than seventy per cent. of the powder and explosive output of the world), the greater number of the army and naval cliques and all those manufacturers interested purely in home and government supply was gaining rapidly. These factions were headed by the Crown Prince and the aggressive feudal aristocracy. The Emperor himself, notwithstanding his paradoxical public attitude as the war lord of Europe, was very much adverse to putting his right to this title to an actual supreme test. He would have much preferred to obtain his ends with saber-rattlings and threats. In any event, his policy was to make war in his own good time.

As yet the sky was clear.

In England conditions were similar. Fiscal policy and preferential tariffs notwithstanding, British trade and commerce was suffering tremendous losses through Germany's commercial enterprises. The rapidly increasing tonnage of the German merchant marine seriously disturbed the British shipping industries, the backbone of Britain's power and wealth. Yearly growing more formidable, the German navy was becoming a distinct menace to England's naval supremacy. Diplomatically England found Germany continually trying with more or less success to break into her jealously-guarded possessions and privileges. Her economic conditions similar to those of Germany were getting into a bad shape with this distinction: whereas Germany overproduced, England did not manufacture and export anything like sufficient quantities to satisfy the demands of her industrial population. The resultant dissatisfaction led to severe strikes, still further aggravating and almost paralyzing her commercial supremacy. Besides all this and in the face of the hundreds of years of peace and quasi-friendship between these two empires and the close relationship between the ruling families,

England's growing jealousy was merging rapidly into open distrust. The tentative advances and propositions of William II for an understanding and alliance were listened to, used to their advantage, and promptly discarded. English diplomacy, often unwarrantedly jeered at (much to England's benefit and the discomfiture of her opponents), proved itself superior to that of Germany. John Bull has a strange faculty of producing at the most needed time men able and fit in every way to offset her usually startling blunders. While Lord Haldane was hobnobbing with the Kaiser and German municipalities were entertaining English civic dignitaries and journalists, Winston Churchill overhauled his fleet and Lord Kitchener took a trip to Belgium. . . .

The result of this was a complete understanding between the General Staffs of England and Belgium. With the knowledge and cooperation of the Belgian government, English army officers, traveling as civilians, were able to make a complete military survey of the country. Beginning with 1909 there was poured into the English General Staff a mass of information about Belgium the like of which for completeness and thoroughness had been equaled by no army, not even the German.

The English knew every square mile of Belgium. They knew the rate of marching their troops could make on every road. Highways suitable for the passage of heavy artillery were marked alongside those unsuitable. The number of Germans in the Belgian manufacturing centers was tabulated, likewise the current of every river and stream, the number of boats, and the number and strength of bridges. The English observers even ascended the steeples of every church in Belgium and marked down how much of the surrounding landscape could be seen, then recommended this or that steeple as an observation post. They knew the condition and number of every kind of railroad wagon in Belgium. Every conceivable bit of information about the railroad systems, even to the different languages that each little station master spoke, was duly recorded. The preparations of the English General Staff went so far that they were able to give the Royal Aviation Corps minutely detailed books which described every available landing place in Belgium. By the spring of 1914 Lord Kitchener possessed information that could have enabled him to have defended Belgium as well as he can defend England.

As yet the sky was clear.

A country about twice the size in area of the United States, with about the same amount of population, with natural resources in coal, iron and other minerals, with lumber forests and arable wheat lands comparable to those which no other land possesses, conscious of its inherent power, slowly but steadily awakening to its commercial possibilities, yet with no outlet for these potentialities: such is Russia.

Time and again since the days of Catherine II (great only in the assimilation of variegated lovers!) has Russia tried to gain an outlet into more convenient, especially warmer waters. She has tried it north and was defeated by Charles XII of Sweden with the assistance of the forebears of the Prussian kings; she has tried it south, and was defeated by England and France through the disinclination of Prussia balancing the scale on her side; she has tried it east and was defeated by Japan which, even with the assistance of England, could never have ousted Russia if Austria at the time, egged on by Germany, had not made aggressive demonstrations against Russia on her Balkan frontiers.

The first visible results of Russia's defeat in the East was the acquisition of Herzegovina and Bosnia by Austria-Hungary, which Russia, without the balance of power in Europe, being seriously disturbed by her weakness, resulting from the eastern fiasco, would never have tolerated. Without doubt, the balance of power underwent a sudden shifting of its scales. Previous to the eastern war Russia was always more or less feared by Germany. It was the unswerving policy of Bismarck, that shrewd judge of European affairs and prince of diplomatic jugglers, to placate and keep on the good side of Russia. Not since the campaigns of Frederick the Great of Prussia during the Seven Years' War were Teuton and Muscovite in actual battle array against each other.

There are in the royal Prussian secret archives in Berlin strict injunctions and instructions as regards Prussian (German) relations toward Russia in the handwriting of Frederick the Great, that past master in diplomatic craft. Were these instructions laid down by an autocratic king regulating, foreseeing and warning his successors against antagonizing the other still more feudal power implicitly followed, there would have been seen unquestionably a different grouping of the powers warring against each other to-day in Europe.

That Germany has looked with envious eyes on Russia is past a doubt. A little more or less of her territory she did not want. But what Germany did desire was such an alliance with Russia that she could hedge and even perhaps dictate her policies. "Russia," said Bismarck, "offers wonderful material for the making of history, let but its feminine type of population be interbred with our strong, masculine Germans." Emperor William, writing in the same vein, gave voice to the opinion that Slavonic people are not a nation, but rather soil on which a nation with a history might grow. Destiny, probably for true freedom, liberty, and for the best of the human race, ordained it otherwise. Just imagine Russia and Germany, the two most autocratic, virile and aggressive powers in the world, going with, instead of against, each other! The possible and probable outcome staggers conception.

Modern German diplomacy, however, saw fit to inaugurate and follow a different course, resulting in the apparent repeated humiliation of Russia. The Muscovite, true to his Tartaric semi-Asiatic origin, never forgets nor forgives. With genuine Asiatic patience and cunning he bided his time, and that time was approaching fast. In the meanwhile, internal disturbances such as the Jewish question (ritual murder), revolutionary outbreaks in Odessa, and general strikes throughout the empire as well as the unsatisfactory financial situation of Russia, gave an apparent impression of total weakness, deceiving to those not intimately well acquainted with the Russian phenomena. For it must be remembered that, without doubt, the most puzzling phenomenon in European affairs has been and is the analogous Russian empire.

William II was not slow in making or trying to make good capital out of Russia's apparent inability to resent Austro-Germanic aggression in the Balkans, a matter that was brought into and explained in "The Secrets of the German War Office" in the Balkan Chapter. Humiliated and resentful, Russia lent a willing ear to Anglo-French overtures. With true Muscovite cunning she prepared for eventualities, as will be seen later, with a secrecy only possible in and understandable by those acquainted with Russia. As previously shown, geographical necessity, a fierce hatred judiciously fostered by Rasputin and the Grand Dukes against all things Teutonic, and the necessity to divert the restless public attention, made Russia a very willing and potential conductor in the highly electrified atmosphere of Europe.

And still the sky was clear.

France of all nations in Europe had no economic or commercial reason to either wish or seek trouble. A characteristic of her sentimental Gallic temperament, the romantic but injudicious habit of decorating the Strassburg monument in Paris, kept ever smoldering a desire to regain the lost provinces. Not that these provinces regained would have made any valuable acquisition, Alsace-Lorraine, very much like Ireland, is a sort of Pandora's box. *Timeo Danaos et dona ferentes*. When they are French they want to be German: when they are German they want to be French. But no one has been able to fathom French sentiment. Geniuses like Richelieu and Bonaparte were able to use this most potent of human emotions without really understanding it, often to the great and temporary advantage of France. Neither of them, however, was able to guard against the inevitable reaction. The consequent result, in common with all violent mental eruptions, was a physical exhaustion, taking the form of super-moral decadence which has as its concomitant a decline in propagation and commercial virility ominously evident in modern France; that is, previous to the outbreak of the war. Uneasily aware of her inability to cope singly with her robust and aggressive northern neighbor, and afraid of a repetition of the days of Sedan and Metz, France was frenziedly willing to enter any alliance promising support and assistance against Germany. To this end France had loaned huge sums of money to Russia, but it was only on the advent of England's joining the Dual Alliance and making it the Entente Cordiale that France felt any sense of security. With characteristic impetuosity, France lost no time in impressing the changed situation upon Germany, with the result that the carefully fostered quarter of a century long endeavor of the German Emperor to placate France was swept away over night and the somewhat bearish good naturedness of Germany toward France reverted to the old antagonism. This reawakened martial spirit in France, assiduously fostered by England, and the personal antagonism of certain French cabinet officers towards His Imperial Majesty, constituted another wire surcharged with positive electricity needing only a requisite point of contact to discharge a pretty solid flash of lightning.

And still the sky was clear.

One of the most anomalous empires of modern times is the Dual Monarchy of Austria-Hungary. It is composed of twenty-six distinct nationalities. Out of a population of 51,000,000, about one-half is Teutonic; of the remainder, Hungary with 21,-000,000 is most of the time, that is, under given circumstances, in sympathy with Teutonic ideas and aspirations. The rest, of Slavonic and Czech origin and tendencies, is diametrically opposed to the Germanic element. Added to this is a section bordering Italy, including the Trentino and Dalmatia, which is purely Italian in intent and proclivities. This conglomerate empire is held together solely by the prestige of the head of the House of Hapsburg, Francis Joseph I; even at that, it has more than once been on the point of disintegration.

The Secrets of the Hohenzollerns

Of the two leading Teutonic royal houses, that of Hohenzollern and that of Hapsburg, the former has outdistanced the latter, often after a bitter and protracted war, as in the case of Frederick the Great's Seven Years' War against Maria Theresa and in 1866 the struggle over the possession of Schleswig-Holstein, ending in the Battle of Koeniggrätz (Sadowa), one of the most bloody battles of modern history.   Notwithstanding this, Prussian diplomacy had gained such an ascendancy over the House of Hapsburg and the affairs of Austria, that Austria has been and is a staunch ally and supported by Germany in all its aims and ambitions.   This alliance is developed to such an extent that even an heir apparent to the Austrian empire unless acceptable to and identified with Prusso-Germanic interests finds it impossible to ascend the throne.

Erzherzog Rudolph, the archduke, next in succession, was mysteriously killed at Mayerling, an obscure little hunting lodge in upper Austria. Much has been written and many conjectures made about the circumstances of this lamentable tragedy.   The real reason, so vast in its importance, has of necessity never been divulged.

On a blustery and cold January night in 1889

The Secrets of the Hohenzollerns

His Royal Highness and the Baroness Marie Vetzera (Vetchera) were familiarly seated around a plain but daintily spread supper table in the hunting lodge of Mayerling. They were attended by Max and Otto K——, two brothers much trusted in the archducal household. Supper was nearly finished and the Prince, who was very fond of a certain brand of champagne, had just given the order to Otto for another couple of bottles, when the deep baying of the Prince's favorite deerhound gave notice of the approach of strangers. A dull thud and the agonized yelp of the dog made the Prince jump up and stride toward the door, which was guarded by Max. Pushing the servant aside, His Royal Highness pulled the door open. Three men muffled up to their eyes in great coats roughly forced their way into the room. In a trice the leader of the trio pinioned Max to the wall. The Archduke, who had jumped back startled and was reseating himself behind the supper table, demanded the reason for this intrusion, when the smallest of the three, supposedly the brother of the Baroness Vetzera, laid hold of a bottle of champagne and brought the weapon down with terrific force on his unprotected head, completely crushing the skull. The

Baroness, who apparently had recognized one of the three intruders, was hysterically screaming and uttering dire threats and vengeance against the perpetrators of this foul deed. As she stood there, gripping the edges of the table, the third, standing at the door, raised his *Stutzen* (a short hunting gun in great favor in the Austrian Alps), and fired point blank at the unfortunate woman, almost blowing her head to pieces.

The commotion brought Otto from the wine cellar, and, taking in the situation at a glance, he threw himself fiercely upon the assassins, ably assisted by his brother Max, who also began attacking his captor. They managed to dispose of one of the assailants when again the gun rang out, sending Max to the floor with his chest almost torn to ribbons. The next moment Otto received a *Hirsch-fänger* (a hunting dagger) between his shoulders. Dragging their wounded conspirator with them, the two assassins disappeared into the night. From that day to this there have never been any arrests made or any one held to account for this dastardly deed.

Otto, who was left for dead, on regaining sufficient strength decently covered the bodies with table cloths and napkins, and left a short pencil written account of the occurrences pinned on to his brother's clothes. He also disappeared in the night; for he well knew the consequences attached to an even entirely innocent witnessing of such a royal family tragedy. Old, gray and bent, Otto is living to this day the quiet life of a hermit and exile not five hundred miles from New York City. Money would never make Otto talk, but some day the upheaval in Europe may provide an occasion when this old retainer of the House of Hapsburg may unseal his lips; and then woe to the guilty.

Rudolph of Hapsburg had to the full the proud instinctive dislike to, and rooted disinclination against, the ever increasing Germanic influence in and over his country. He died.[1]

A cipher telegram handed into Captain von Tapken visibly perturbed this usually very unruffled gentleman, and such was his agitation that he immediately left for the Wilhelmstrasse to consult with Count Wedell, the Emperor's Secret

[1] The above account of the tragedy of Mayerling, notwithstanding the "proof" of the Crown Prince's supposed suicide contained in the letters alleged to have been written by him to his confidant and friend Ambassador Szoegyenyi and to the "Duke of Braganza," is the correct one, and will be proved when the venerable head of the House of Hapsburg shall have passed away.

THE AUTHOR.

Service Chief. The Count likewise stared blankly at the translation and after a few hasty orders, hurried to the castle to consult his royal master. This cipher telegram was evidently of startling importance. The German Secret Service agent in Belgium had ascertained that a certain English party was making an extended tour of travel and inspection through Belgium. Any party interested in Prussian, Belgian and Franco-Belgian border affairs is likewise interesting to the powers in Berlin. If it includes such eminent men as the English party did, it receives their thorough and undivided attention. Here was Lord Kitchener accompanied by some of the leading military experts and draughtsmen of the British army touring up and down the Belgian frontiers. Berlin was asking itself: Why? To inspect the dairies? No! Lord Kitchener does not interest himself in cows. Why the presence of these expert draughtsmen? To paint quaint pictures of the canals and dykes? No! Lord Kitchener does not permit British army officers to dabble in paint. Then why?

The news of this inspection came on top of indisputable information but lately gained that the Belgian forts of Liège, Namur, etc., were heavily

PRINCE VON BUELOW

Former chancellor and intimate friend of the Kaiser, who,
notwithstanding his friendship, was forced to retire

strengthened at an approximate cost of two millions of francs, of which only one-third was provided by the Belgian government. Who had furnished the rest? Paraguay or Ecuador? No wonder Berlin was somewhat disturbed.

The House of Brabant, distinctly French in sympathies and at no time over friendly to the Hohenzollerns, was represented by an unusually clever and courageous king. King Albert of Belgium is also ambitious. This ambition was shrewdly used by France and England to the furtherance of their policies.

The sky was not quite so clear.

In a moment of more then usually pronounced *lapsus mentis* the Austrian powers that be decided on a Crown Princely visit to the lately acquired provinces of Herzegovina and Bosnia. It was probably the idea and intention to instil some much needed patriotism into these extremely unwilling must-be Hapsburgers. Under even ordinary circumstances, this visit would have been ill-advised. In the face of existent conditions, the unsettled state of these provinces and the fomenting trouble with Serbia, it was nothing short of criminal. One is almost led to believe that the Government actually courted some such catastrophe as actually happened; or else the men whose business it should be to know these things must have been more than ordinarily stupid. The result of this ill-fated state visit was the assassination of the Arch Duke of Austria and his consort. That in itself was shocking and bad enough. The furiously bitter attitude of the Austrian people towards Serbia, the supposed instigator of the assassination, made it worse. The extremely harsh and unrelenting personal demands of Francis Joseph I brought it to a breaking point.

A blue-black, sinister-looking cloud was appearing on the southern horizon.

Forty-eight hours after the Austrian ultimatum was presented to the Serbian government, Rasputin, the Tsar's familiar, accompanied by the son of the Grand Duke Nicholas, left the Peterhof, the summer residence of the Tsar. Tucked away in his cassock was a ukase personally signed by the Tsar, ordering every commander along the entire Russo-Austrian frontiers to prepare with the utmost speed and secrecy their respective stations. So craftily did Rasputin go about this

mission that even the argus-eyed German Secret
Service failed to detect anything unusual until
up to four days before the actual outbreak of hostilities. When finally they did obtain conclusive
proofs of Russian activity, Emperor William
sent his famous ultimatum to the Tsar, giving
Russia exactly four days' time for decision, the
Emperor using the four days' limit as a hint to
Russia that her secret mobilization was already
known in Berlin.

Allied with Rasputin the Grand Duke Nicolai
Nicolaievitch was ruling Russia. A man of
boundless ambition, shrewd, but more moral than
the Grand Dukes that Paris knows, Nicolai is the
one big man in Russia. He wants to be the Tsar.
The Russian Emperor knows that; so does Rasputin. Rasputin does not want him to be Tsar.
It would mean that Rasputin's power would be
curtailed. Rasputin could not handle a man like
Nicolai Nicolaievitch. Ruler of the army, Nicolai studied the lessons of the Japanese war and
made it a new army. Artillery fascinated him,
which is why the Russian artillery is to-day effi-
cient. War also fascinated him. War would
make him an even greater hero with his army.

Some day with the army at his back—who knows?

When the Tsar ordered Nicolai to evacuate Warsaw before the invasion of Hindenburg, Nicolai sent word that if the Tsar insisted he would withdraw his forces—but he would march at the head of his army to Petrograd. The Tsar told him to hold Warsaw.

Wanting war, Nicolai had an understanding with Rasputin. Perhaps he showed himself a little cleverer than Rasputin. This chance to make himself a popular hero might open the way to the throne, which would mean the fall of Rasputin's power. Or did Rasputin think to kill two birds, to take his revenge upon the German Emperor and to break the Grand Duke by a disastrous war —who knows?

It has become known though, through the underground channels of Europe, that Nicolai made the Tsar a prisoner in his own castle. With the support of the court, that was afraid of him and that was contemptuous of the Tsar, Nicolai compelled the Little Father to continue to flaunt war in the face of Germany.

A purple-black cloud was rushing over the western horizon.

The Secrets of the Hohenzollerns

South and west storm clouds were banking; east and west an ominous muttering was heard; denser and denser became the atmosphere; the whole of Europe was gasping and trembling before this approaching storm. It needed only the Austrian Emperor's declaration of war against Serbia to set the mass of clouds rushing at each other and discharging a flood of electricity that threatened to strike the whole of Europe to the heart's core. The black box of the old Hohenzollerns was unlocked; the Emperor was ready to go to war.

CHAPTER XII

THE UNACCOUNTED FACTOR

IT is an old saying that curses, like chickens, come home to roost. In the same manner do ill-advised diplomatic *faux-pas* invariably result for the perpetrator in situations often very dangerous. It is inexplicable but nevertheless a fact that Germany, up-to-date, scientific and studious in all other things, has made in her diplomatic relations some very palpable and disastrous blunders.

The utter astonishment of the greater mass of the German people at the rather unsympathetic, not to say antagonistic, attitude entertained by Americans toward the Fatherland borders almost on naïveté. But Germany has no one save herself to blame for this unsympathetic feeling toward her by the American people. Americans have the very commendable habit of minding their own business. At the same time, they possess a rooted dislike and resentment to any interference, however slight, in continental American affairs. This dislike is clearly shown in the promulgation of the Monroe Doctrine. On the other hand, Americans, who as a rule have no great love or liking for England, are showing to-day a distinct sentimental partiality toward Great Britain. The reasons, although evidently overlooked by Germany, present no difficulty in tracing. The following incidents may benefit those whose voices are raised so loudly against this very natural attitude of the greater number of Americans:

Although Germany has become nearly the leading commercial nation in the world, deriving therefrom most of her wealth and power, the men of influence with different ideals, aims and ambitions were disposed to look down upon all other more purely commercial nations with a sort of contemptuous indifference as to their capability of ever becoming a military factor to be reckoned with. To no country has Germany shown this contempt more than to America. This is, of course, meant in a purely military sense; the wealth and power of the United States in other matters was always fully recognized by Germany.

This haughtily scornful attitude received a mild shock through the belligerent disposition and drastic manner with which the United States went into and handled the Cuban question. So displeasing was this revelation of Yankee militarism to the powers at the Wilhelmstrasse that, without being in any way interested in the *casus belli* and admittedly holding no brief for Spain, they still saw fit to try to intimidate the United States in favor of Spain. The Emperor could not brook the idea of a republic trying to best a monarchy. Republics are one of the German Emperor's pet aversions. How dared a plain, ordinary human being, even if seated in the White House, threaten and declare war against one of the Lord's anointed! We, Wilhelm, by and with the Grace of God, will see! He did see; in fact, unless blind, he is seeing still.

The sending of a German squadron to Manila Bay was one of the worst personal blunders of which William II has ever been guilty. It was an added unfortunate circumstance that the German officer in command, Admiral von Dietrich, a rather short-tempered, arrogant martinet, bore a personal grudge against Admiral Dewey, the commander of the United States fleet. Without doubt Admiral von Dietrich exceeded his instructions; nevertheless, the whole business was a grievous mistake, which is bearing bitter fruit to this day.

The resentment of the American people soon made itself felt in Germany. The Emperor, endeavoring to make good his mistake, approached McKinley, suggesting a visit by his brother to the United States. The quiet, unassuming, thoroughly American gentleman at the White House received this suggestion with no enthusiasm. Under the next administration the overtures met with more success, however, and promptly His Royal Highness, Prince Henry of Prussia, brother to the Emperor of Germany and Commander-in-Chief of the German Highsea Fleets, appeared on the scene.

From beginning to end, the vist of His Royal Highness was a huge success. The genial affability and sailorly tact and bearing of the Prince made him a universal favorite. He was fêted, dined and wined from one end of the country to the other. American society trotted out its best frocks and largest diamonds much to the goggle-eyed astonishment of some of the Prussian aristocrats. "Diamond tiaras for breakfast? Hm! Great people, the Americans! Eh, what, *Kamerad?*"

The Secrets of the Hohenzollerns

Prince Henry was extremely democratic while in the United States. He shook hands with any and everybody and went through stunts such as the filling of glasses at a famous dinner party, the driving of an express train in greasy overalls, and the high jinks at the New York Metropolitan Club dinner, that would have made his illustrious brother's eyes water.

At the last mentioned memorable occasion, the Prince no doubt had the time of his life. The late J. P. Morgan had invited about twenty-five of his most intimate cronies to meet His Royal Highness at a stag dinner party at the Metropolitan Club. The royal barouche with the Prince and his friend Bob Evans, closely followed by the hansom occupied by his bodyguard, dashed through the gates, which were immediately closed and locked. Prince Henry was received by his host, and, after mutual introductions, sojourned to the bar where three Scotch and sodas were imbibed in as many minutes. Stories, snappy and crisp, began to circulate, there being present some past masters in the art of telling stories with the *pointe delicate*. The Scotch and stories created a pretty torrid temperature, and J. P. Morgan, beginning to feel rather pent up in his stiff full dress coat, suggested peeling off this cumbersome badge of respectability. This was received with fervid acclamations. The Prince, after a startled glance at his guide and mentor, Bob Evans, who, whimsically grinning began peeling off his coat, shed his garment with a relieved, "Rather odd, Evans, but damned comfortable all the same."

More Scotch and soda.

Then the great financier announced dinner in the following classical words, "Come on, boys, and grab some eats." They did "grab the eats," for the world's best food and wine was to be had for the grabbing.

The center of the table was covered with an enormous paper doily folded in the form of a bishop's mitre surrounded by masses of American Beauty roses. The dishes were scarcely removed and the glasses filled up than the host rose and cautioned his table companions, "Boys, grab what's coming and grab it quick."

Pressing a button, the paper doily broke and, on a rising platform appeared ten of the most beauteous maidens. With a roar of applause the hostly injunction was obeyed. Nor was the Prince the last to join the fun.

All this may seem very shocking to those not

accustomed to cosmopolitan experience. For a matter of fact, however, there was no hint of license or vulgarity in the surprise. It was one of those occasions where jollity and good fellowship reign supreme, occasions that bring men of that stamp closer together in five minutes than stiff diplomacy or high finance would in five years. The Prince had a bully good time; but one would like to picture His Imperial brother's face if he could have seen Heinrich sitting in shirt sleeves with his collar wilted, clinking glasses, singing songs, and, most of all, hugely enjoying it.[1]

Amongst the princely baggage was a trunk full of souvenirs and orders. There was no lack of willing recipients; in fact, the story is current that towards the end of the itinerary some of the Prince's suite were obliged to part with their minor decorations to still the heartache of a certain Krieger-Vereine President of Chicago. Strange this desire for titles and decorations in an avowed democratic republic! Is it possible

[1] The absolute authenticity of the above incident occurring during the Prince Henry's visit is vouched for and corroborated by the leading member of the Prince's bodyguard while in New York: Detective-Sergeant William M. Duggan, now Captain of Police.

that William II is right after all? One wonders, wonders, wonders. . . .

This visit, let it be remembered, was purely one of friendship and good will. Nevertheless Germany never neglects a single opportunity to obtain valuable information and this American tour was no exception. In the Prince's suite were experts of various kinds who made full use of their powers. The following incident is illuminating.

The Prince was reviewing the German-American Krieger-Vereine, Sänger-Bünde and allied associations of New York. Steadily to martial music the massed thousands were swinging past. When the last line had filed by, one of the Prince's aides snapped his watch close and, saluting, reported, "Ninety-seven minutes, Your Royal Highness." Immediately a second officer reported, "Sixty-six thousand five hundred."

This close scrutiny, timing and counting was followed in every city visited. It was reported and noted that by the end of his visit Prince Henry had reviewed three hundred and twenty thousand Germans, mostly of the ages between twenty-five and forty.

If Germany has neglected to account the sentiment of America as a neutral commercial factor, the direct possibilities of the United States entering the war have *not* been lost sight of by the master minds of the General Staff. There are docketed in their respective pigeonholes in the archives of the Grosse (General) Stab more correct data on American army and navy matters than congressional investigators and committees are able to obtain. They have more correct statistics of the number of Germans resident in the United States, their organizations, etc., than will be found in the official census bureau in Washington. According to their information there are 13,476,000 German-Americans, of whom 3,160,-000 were born German citizens. Out of this number 285,000 are trained men and reservists. The possession of such information was perhaps responsible for the German belief in America's sympathy in her cause. Likewise Americans should study these figures in all seriousness, for who knows what the times may bring forth?

The success of the princely visit helped to a great extent to obscure the Manila incident and reestablish friendly relations. Another very potent factor was the sympathetic feeling between the Administration and the Court at Berlin, for was not Alice Roosevelt received with royal honors? Emperor William and Colonel Roosevelt, the then President, have very much in common. Both are strong men, both are great believers in themselves, and both are great opportunists. Those two men could understand and appreciate each other.

The decidedly favorable attitude toward Germany lasted throughout the Roosevelt administration. Unfortunately, however, Germany did not follow up her good lead. The Emperor and his advisers, keenly alive to most of the equations in the art of successful government, have always neglected the force and value of public opinion in other countries save their own. The Emperor does not believe in *vox populi, vox Dei.*

Contrary to her usual policy but with clever farsightedness, England has managed to change the inherent dislike of the Americans, if not exactly to regard, at least to a good deal of substantial sympathy. This is the result of carefully planned and executed social and press campaigns dating back at least four years. The often belittled and sneered at inter-marriages between the plutocracy of America and the aristocracy of England have brought profitable results, at least for Great Britain. With unusual forbearance and tolerance England has refrained during the last decade from irritating the people of the United States. In innumerable small ways, singly insignificant, collectively of great importance, the two countries have become more and more friendly. The "beastly Yankee" became a "bally American," and "Uncle Sam" changed into "Brother Jonathan" and "Hands Across the Sea."

England with shrewd farsightedness, well knowing and fully recognizing the importance of public opinion, carefully prepared the way. Germany, underrating the practical value of this opinion, neglected it almost entirely, a piece of shortsightedness likely to change the whole trend of affairs as far as Germany is concerned.

The Great General Staff in Berlin knew the general unpreparedness of England and her allies and was convinced of their inability to produce arms and ammunition in sufficient quantities to equip the possible number of men they could put in the field, or to make good the wastes resulting from a war. It seems never to have entered into their calculations that outside nations would be able to supply in any appreciable amount the needed war materials. Least of all were the United States considered able or likely to become a factor as a source of supply. In too closely watching Europe, Germany had almost entirely neglected keeping herself informed on the possibilities of the private ammunition and small arms concerns of the United States. In any event, it was considered unlikely that the United States, having no direct interests at stake, would assist either one party or the other. Satisfied that she herself needed no assistance, Germany believed that a balance of opinion would keep the States from assisting the other nations. In short, the United States remaining neutral was not considered a factor.

It is the old case of the rift within the lute. The hundreds of millions' worth of materials of all descriptions bought by the Allies here in America will prove a very deciding factor in the outcome of the struggle in Europe. Germany has been realizing this too late, and all the frenzied newspaper and other campaigns and counter-campaigns will not alter this state of affairs. The senseless attacks on the United States government, especially on the heads of the Administration by hyphenated sympathizers of either side, are simply a waste of effort, the only likely result being bitterness and ill-feeling amongst themselves. At a time when the rest of the world is evidently suffering from a virulent species of animus insanity, it is absolutely necessary for the American people to be wholly in accord amongst themselves. This internal peace can best be maintained by refusing to recognize any other claims or interests save those of their own country, and by staunchly supporting the Chief Executive in his policy of keeping out of all strife.

Some day when the high waves of feeling shall have subsided, and the now conflicting interests have found a more common level, the excellent attitude and position taken by President Wilson as regards the relations of the United States with the warring powers will give him a place in the history of this country on a level with those of Washington and Lincoln. To keep a vastly rich and powerful country, teeming with over ninety million people mostly composed of descendants of men from the present belligerent European countries, from rushing headlong into war and consequent incalculable misery and loss, is truly a herculean task. What an amount of conflicting influence and pressure is brought to bear upon the Chief Executive of the most powerful neutral country on earth is known only to himself. But there is every reason to believe that the level-headed, truly clean American at the White House will go uninfluenced the even tenor of his way, strong in the convictions that his stand is the only sane one to take for the best interests of his country.

The Sphinx of the White House is a true symbol of America, the unaccounted factor.

CHAPTER XIII

THE ANSWER

THE *telefunken* expert, Heinrich Drechsel, was sitting at his instrument in the wireless tower at Kiel idly listening to the various conversations passing invisibly through the ether.

"Click! Click! Click! S.M.I. . . . S.M.I. . . . S.M.I. . . ."

Idleness was gone. Alert, with a few deft manipulations of his tuning keys, he answered the call, sending out the silence order at the same instant.

"S.M.I." preceded every other call in Germany. It is the Emperor's code signal.

Dots . . . dashes . . . and numerals were pouring in from the Berlin station. It was his duty to transmit them to the *Hohenzollern* steaming somewhere about the Norwegian coast. . . .

"Pss! Cackle! Crackle! Pss!" sputtered the instrument on board *Seine Majestät Schiff Hohenzollern.*

The Secrets of the Hohenzollerns

A bell tinkled.

The officer in charge of the wireless room, who was playing skat with his two comrades, laid down his hand and clapped on the receiver. With a grimace, he remarked, "More messages from the Spassvogelchen." It is a standing joke on board the *Hohenzollern* that not a day passes but that the Emperor receives a dozen messages from his only daughter, who usually sends all sorts of funny titbits which earned her the sobriquet of *Spassvogel* (the Joking Bird).

The grin disappeared and with a sharp, "Attention. . . . Number One, to your station. Number Two, to your desk," the officer bent his attention to his task.

Sharp and quickly the numbers flowed from his lips to be immediately taken down and translated by the other two.

"F.F.F." sputtered the instrument, and became silent. Blankly the three men looked at each other. With a white face and a muttered, "Oh Hell!" the officer in charge rushed out of the cabin to the Emperor's quarters.

Within three minutes the bow of the *Hohenzollern* was turned due south, racing at full speed for home waters. . . .

The Secrets of the Hohenzollerns

Dark and silent, six of the fastest German torpedo boat destroyers were plowing along the north coast of Denmark, on the bridge the commander of each with night glasses glued to his eyes. It was their duty to pick up the *Hohenzollern* and convoy her safely into port.

On the horizon a white ghost-like hull, a white bone in her teeth—the feathered seawash of a fast-going vessel.

Two green balls and a red answered by two red balls and a green.

The destroyers swung to. One ahead. One astern. Two on each side.

On they swept. . . .

On the imperial landing pier of the naval yards in Kiel two groups of men awaited the coming of the *Hohenzollern*. In front, Frederick Wilhelm, Crown Prince of Germany and heir apparent to the throne, with his uncle Henry of Prussia, Commander-in-Chief of the German Highsea Fleets. In the second group the tall spare figure of von Bethmann-Hollweg, Chancellor of the German Empire, was easily distinguished. Standing close to him were two equally easily recognized personages, von Tirpitz, Grand Admiral of the German navy, and von Moltke, Chief of Staff of the Imperial army.

They were conversing in whispers, casting anxious glances toward the entrance of the harbor.

The booming salute of the outer guardship drew a relieved, "Ah! at last."

Without coming to anchor, the *Hohenzollern* dropped a hooded barcasse which speeded to the landing. The groups moved forward and silently saluted the solitary figure emerging from the boat. A quick handshake with son and brother, and the Emperor taking von Hollweg's arm entered the awaiting auto and was driven top speed to his special train.

It is a significant fact that the Emperor was in Berlin twenty-four hours before his return was officially acknowledged. . . .

In the General Staff building in Berlin there is a small, dingy, unpretentious room where at moments of stress and tension of international complications, assemble five men. His Majesty, the Emperor of Germany, Commander-in-Chief of all the German armies, sits at the head of a plain oblong oak table; to the right, the Chief of the General Staff; to the left, His Minister of War;

then the Chief of the Admiralty Staff and the Minister of Railways. When those five men meet, the influence of the diplomatic and financial affairs has ceased. They are there to act. The scratching of the Emperor's pen in that room means war, the setting in motion of a fighting force of 5,000,000 men.

Four men were already assembled in this room. Von Moltke, von Tirpitz, General von Heeringen and von Wackerzapp were awaiting the entrance of the Emperor. William II was closeted in strict seclusion with the head of the House of Ehrenkrug and the Imperial Chancellor.

The door opened. The Emperor entered, escorted by the two above-named men. Standing at the head of the table he looked first at Ehrenkrug, then at Hollweg, and in a distinct voice asked, "I have your message, and you have mine. The answer?"

Ehrenkrug, stepping forward and taking the Emperor's right hand repeated slowly and solemnly three times, "Do thou thy duty as thy forebears have done before thee." Bending low he kissed the Emperor's hand, saluted the others and left.

The scratch of a pen.

Europe ran red.

CHAPTER XIV

VIA VICTIS

AFTER nine months of unprecedented slaughter, inconceivable sacrifices and efforts on all sides, the situation is this: Germany holds the whole of Belgium, a goodly strip of northern France and strategic positions in Russian Poland. There is at present no enemy within eighty kilometers of any German territory. Possession of Belgium and the occupation of the northern French provinces give Germany a decided advantage. The main efforts of the Allies, especially of England, are to thrash the German army back on to German territory and compel the relinquishing of Belgium. If they will be successful in this, time only will show; there is not the slightest doubt that Germany, well realizing the enormous importance of its present positions, will do its utmost to prevent the Allies from gaining their point. That Germany has not the slightest intention of reinstating Belgium as an independent kingdom goes without question; all reiterations to the contrary notwithstanding.

Although Germany has sustained frightful injuries through the loss of her colonies, the temporary smashing of her commerce and the rapid expenditure of her accumulated wealth, the possession of Belgium is no mean recompense. If Germany does not gain anything else in this present struggle, the possession of Belgium will well repay her for her sacrifices.

First and last Germany needed additional outlets to the North Sea for her ever-growing overseas commerce. In the magnificently placed harbors of the Belgian seaboard, she has found these needed outlets. Strategically, the possession of Belgium by Germany means the death knell to British Channel supremacy. With the added shipping facilities of Antwerp, etc., German commerce, although almost completely interrupted at present, would in no time regain more than its old strength. All this is well understood in the cabinets of the Allies. They know that the only hope of Belgian independence is in their ability to beat Germany out of this territory by force of arms. No diplomatic juggling will ever be able to attain this end, for what Germany has, she will hold. The only power she will recognize is a superiority in shot and shell.

Years ago the author heard discussions between leading members of the German General Staff foreshadowing events which have been and are taking place daily. Even as far back as 1902 complete plans and estimates as to the probable cost of men and money in the acquisition of Belgium were discussed and calmly gone into. Every possible combination against Germany, even those actually in existence now, was considered, and Germany's chances of success carefully weighed. These men had sat day by day, week by week, month by month, and year by year studying and dissecting every possible phase of pro and con in this present struggle for Continental supremacy. They had then and do now consider no effort or sacrifice too dear to provide Germany with an additional pair of lungs on the North Sea. Years ago the taking of Belgium under certain circumstances was prepared for and the holding of Belgium once taken more so still. Germany has made for years concerted efforts and tried her utmost to induce Belgium to join the German Confederation of States, much in the same manner and with the same privileges as did the Kingdom of Bavaria previous to the Franco-Prussian War. There was a time when these German endeavors almost bore fruit, but the antagonism and private ambition of the royal house of Belgium, judiciously encouraged and fostered by England, frustrated the German plans. The main instrument in calling checkmate to German diplomacy in the Lowlands was the astute Bohemian, Edward VII. Belgium, with the usual wisdom and snappy pugnacity of the small dog in fawning to the big mastiff, but surreptitiously trying to abstract a few titbits from the big one's food plate, was trying to run with both packs of wolves. As usually happens in cases of this kind of mental and physical acrobatics, they result mostly in a broken spine. Belgium has evidently never learned that one pets and pities a small dog, but one does not interfere with the big dog's quarrel. But the lamentable state of Belgium to-day does not justify the German scheme of action. For this cannot be gainsaid: that Germany wanted Belgium, gave her a chance to walk into subjection, and that opportunity being refused, went about the seizure of Belgium with systematic ruthlessness. The blot is on the escutcheon of Germany and eventually she will pay in more ways than one for her disregard of treaties and solemn pacts.

Meantime this does not affect the situation. There will be a goodly number of other people besides the Belgians whose eyes will be opened when the peace pacts of Europe are signed. When that time comes, if Germany still holds Belgium, England's own vital interests will be so endangered that the independence of Belgium in any case interesting to England only by reason of her danger of a too close proximity of possible German naval stations, will be relegated very much to the background. It will be the old, old story of each for himself and the devil take the hindmost. The Hotel de Ville in Brussels is flying the German eagle. That eagle is likely to roost there for many a day.

THE END

Popular Copyright Novels

AT MODERATE PRICES

Ask your dealer for a complete list of
A. L. Burt Company's Popular Copyright Fiction

Popular Copyright Novels

AT MODERATE PRICES

Ask your dealer for a complete list of
A. L. Burt Company's Popular Copyright Fiction

Popular Copyright Novels

AT MODERATE PRICES

Ask your dealer for a complete list of
A. L. Burt Company's Popular Copyright Fiction

Popular Copyright Novels

AT MODERATE PRICES

Ask your dealer for a complete list of
A. L. Burt Company's Popular Copyright Fiction

Hidden Children, The.............*Robert W. Chambers*
Highway of Fate, The...................*Rosa N. Carey*
Homesteaders, The...........*Kate and Virgil D. Boyles*
Hoosier Volunteer, The........*Kate and Virgil D. Boyles*
Hopalong Cassidy.................*Clarence E. Mulford*
House of Happiness, The..........*Kate Langley Bosher*
House of the Whispering Pines............*A. K. Green*
Hugh Wynne, Free Quaker.........*S. W. Mitchell, M.D.*
Husbands of Edith, The........*George Barr McCutcheon*
Illustrious Prince, The............*E Phillips Oppenheim*
Imposter, The.........................*John Reed Scott*
In Defiance of the King.........*Chauncey C. Hotchkiss*
Indifference of Juliet, The...........*Grace S. Richmond*
Inez (Ill. Ed.).......................*Augusta J. Evans*
Infelice.........................*Augusta Evans Wilson*
Initials Only....................*Anna Katharine Green*
Innocent ....*Marie Corelli*
Intriguers, The........................*Harold Bindloss*
Iron Trail, The.............................*Rex Beach*
Iron Woman, The...................*Margaret Deland*
Ishmael (Ill.).........................*Mrs. Southworth*
Island of Regeneration, The......*Cyrus Townsend Brady*
Island of the Stairs, The.........*Cyrus Townsend Brady*
Japonette.......................*Robert W. Chambers*
Jane Cable.................*George Barr McCutcheon*
Jeanne of the Marshes............*E. Phillips Oppenheim*
Jennie Gerhardt......................*Theodore Dreiser*
Joyful Heatherby........................*Payne Erskine*
Jude the Obscure.......................*Thomas Hardy*
Judgment House, The..................*Gilbert Parker*
Keith of the Border...................*Randall Parrish*
Kent Knowles: "Quahaug"............*Joseph C. Lincoln*
Kingsmead.........................*Bettina Von Hutten*
Knave of Diamonds, The.................*Ethel M. Dell*
Ladder of Swords, A......................*Gilbert Parker*
Lady and the Pirate, The...............*Emerson Hough*
Lady Betty Across the Water *C. N. and A. M. Williamson*
Lady Merton, Colonist............*Mrs. Humphry Ward*
Land of Long Ago, The.............*Eliza Calvert Hall*
Last Shot, The....................*Frederick N. Palmer*

Popular Copyright Novels

AT MODERATE PRICES

Ask your dealer for a complete list of
A. L. Burt Company's Popular Copyright Fiction

Popular Copyright Novels

AT MODERATE PRICES

Ask your dealer for a complete list of
A. L. Burt Company's Popular Copyright **Fiction**

Popular Copyright Novels

AT MODERATE PRICES

Ask your dealer for a complete list of
A. L. Burt Company's Popular Copyright Fiction

Popular Copyright Novels

AT MODERATE PRICES

Ask your dealer for a complete list of
A. L. Burt Company's Popular Copyright Fiction

Popular Copyright Novels

AT MODERATE PRICES

Ask your dealer for a complete list of
A. L. Burt Company's Popular Copyright Fiction

Popular Copyright Novels

AT MODERATE PRICES

Ask your dealer for a complete list of
A. L. Burt Company's Popular Copyright Fiction